THE UNIVERSE

THE
UNIVERSE

A VOYAGE THROUGH SPACE AND TIME

Nigel Henbest

Photography
Philip Chudy

Weidenfeld and Nicolson
London

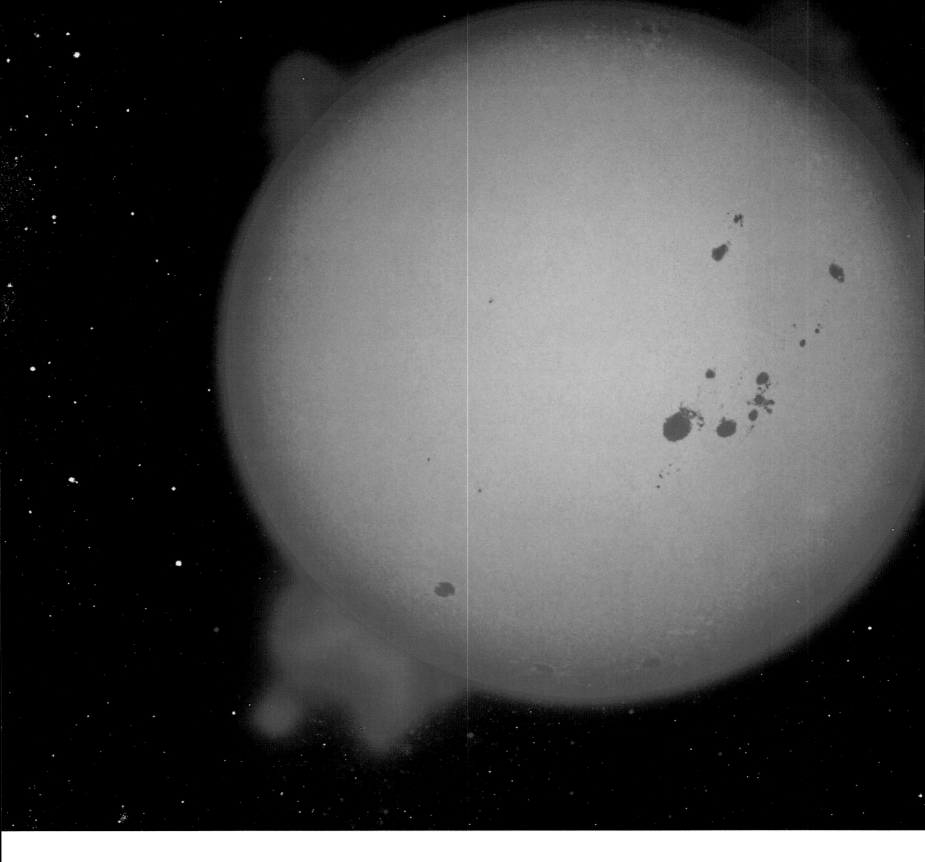

First published in Great Britain in 1992 by
George Weidenfeld & Nicolson Ltd
91 Clapham High Street, London SW4 7TA

Editor: Elizabeth Drury
Design and typesetting: Eric Drewery
Artwork: Rodney Paull and Sebastian Quigley (Linden Artists)
Reproduction by Columbia Offset Ltd.

Created and produced by Roxby Paintbox Company Ltd,
126 Victoria Rise, London SW4 0NW

ISBN 0297 831100

Printed and bound in Spain by Cayfosa

CONTENTS

LONG AGO AND FAR AWAY
6

The Big Bang 8

The Structure of the Universe 10

Galaxies Start to Form 12

Quasars 14

Expanding Galaxies 16

Different Kinds of Galaxy 18

Close Encounters between Galaxies 20

Galactic Cannibalism 22

THE MIDDLE DISTANCE
24

The Milky Way 26

A Star is Born 28

Proto-stars 30

Stars in their Prime 32

Stars in Middle Age 34

Star Death 36

Relics in Space 38

Rebirth of a Star 40

HERE AND NOW
42

Birth of the Planets 44

Comets 46

Pluto: the Frontier Planet 48

Water and Gas Planets 50

Rings 52

Moons 54

Mercury: the Fossil Planet 56

Mars: the Ice Age World 58

Venus: the Hell Planet 60

The Big Splash 62

Earth: the Living Planet 64

THE FUTURE
66

Death of the Sun 68

Death of the Milky Way 70

The End of the Universe 72

Forward to the Past 74

Glossary 76

Chronology 78

Photographing the Unseen 79

Index 80

LONG AGO AND FAR AWAY

15 billion to 10 billion years ago

In the beginning, there was no time. There was no space. There was no matter. Space and time did not exist.

For a reason that we do not understand, the Universe suddenly *was*. Time began to flow. Space was created, and it swelled in size. Matter came into being, and was carried away in the expansion of space. The result was the Big Bang.

This titanic eruption happened some 15,000 million years ago. The debris from the Big Bang has expanded to become the Universe we know today. Some of the matter in the Universe has changed, but the basic material of the stars, the planets, the Earth – and ourselves – was spawned in the unparalleled violence of the Big Bang.

Many of the most important scenes in the drama of the Universe were played out relatively soon after its birth – well before the Earth was born. The clouds of hot gas from the Big Bang formed into stars, which were clumped into great star-islands, called galaxies. Galaxies collided; they grew fatter by feeding on gas or by swallowing up one another; fountains of energy – quasars – erupted in the centres of the galaxies.

All this happened long before people were around to witness the events. But astronomers can now dig into the long-dead past of the Universe, using a whole variety of telescopes as time machines. A telescope collects light (or other radiations) from space, and these radiations take time to travel to us. The light we see from the Sun, for example, left it just over eight minutes ago. The light from the brighter night-time stars has been on its way for several decades: the more distant stars we see may no longer even exist.

The Universe of galaxies is much vaster, and we can peer far deeper into time. With the naked eye, we can see the Andromeda Galaxy – as it was two million years ago, when the first humans were treading the Earth.

The largest of modern telescopes can show distant parts of the Universe as they existed soon after the Big Bang. The view through a telescope gives us only a blurred and tantalizing glimpse of that exciting time. But astronomers have been able to wring enough information from these drops of light and other radiations to build up a good idea of how the early Universe would have looked, if we could have been there to witness the Big Bang and its immediate aftermath.

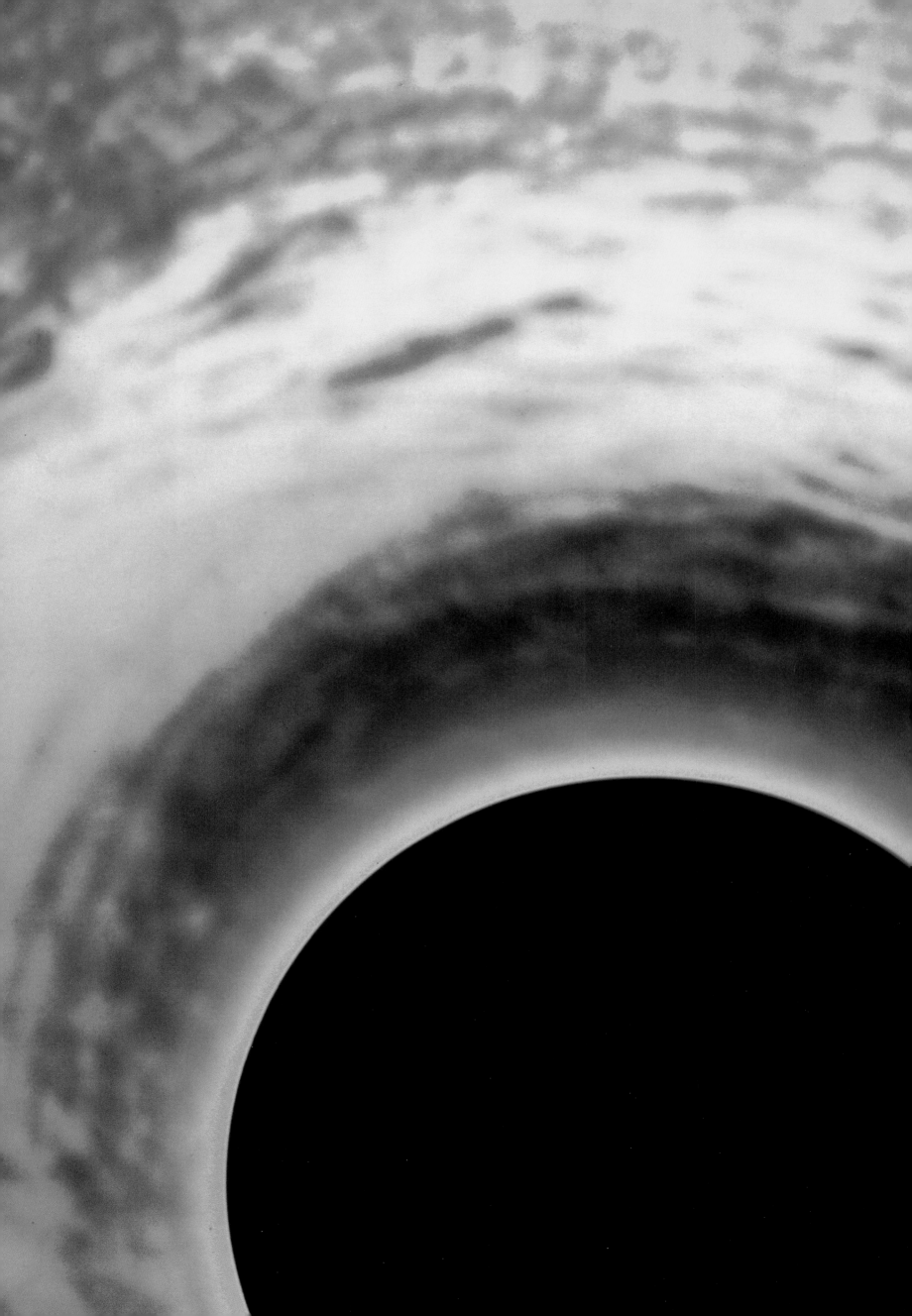

THE BIG BANG

The Universe sprang from a tiny speck of matter, smaller than an atom. This 'primeval atom' was hot – over a million million million times hotter than the core of the Sun. Its pent-up energy forced it to expand. Because all of space was contained within it, this primeval atom could not blow outwards into its surroundings: there was no space outside itself. The expansion of the atom was more like a balloon being blown up. Space itself grew bigger, spreading out like the skin of a balloon.

At this stage, the Universe contained very little matter – perhaps no more than the contents of a bag of sugar. And the expansion was gentle. So where did all the matter of the Universe today come from, and why is the Universe now expanding as if it has been thrown out by a giant explosion?

An American physicist, Alan Guth, discovered the answer in 1981. The hot gases in the very young Universe did not consist of matter as we know it. At these temperatures, atoms – and even their constituents, such as protons and neutrons – did not exist. Forces such as gravity and magnetism could not exist as we know them. Matter and forces were blended into a uniform mush, so that each was indistinguishable from the other. But the Universe was cooling all the time, and – Guth realized – at some point the matter and forces must adopt the forms we find today.

At that time, the Universe was in a unique state, as it never had been before and never would be again. According to Guth's calculations, as the matter and forces took on their own identity, gravity – for a short while – went through a strange and wayward phase. Today, gravity is a force that always pulls things together but, at this point in the Universe's early history, gravity was briefly a force that pushed matter apart.

The intense gravity of the early Universe turned the slow expansion of space into a gigantic explosion. Astronomers call this the 'inflationary period' of the Universe's history. This period, when gravity ripped the Universe apart, was the Big Bang.

The negative forces of gravity at this time could also create new matter in the Universe: it sprang into existence to compensate for the gulfs left as space itself expanded at an alarming rate. In this first fraction of a second, the original few kilograms of the Universe's material multiplied into all the matter that forms the galaxies today.

Once the period of inflation was over, the Universe contained the familiar forces such as electricity and magnetism – and gravity that pulls objects together. The matter was in less familiar forms. There were quarks, which then formed together in threes to make protons and neutrons – particles that survived to make up the centres of all atoms that exist today. There were also electrons, which would eventually join with the other particles to form complete atoms.

But the hostile hot environment also contained anti-matter. When anti-matter meets matter, the result is annihilation. Battle between matter and anti-matter was joined within the first one second of the Universe's life. If the amounts on both sides had been exactly equal, there would have been total destruction of the matter, and the Universe today would contain no galaxies, no stars and no planets. As it happened, the matter was almost destroyed, but not quite. For every 100,000,000 particles of matter there were only 99,999,999 particles of anti-matter, so small amounts of matter won through after the great annihilation.

The annihilation produced copious amounts of heat and radiation, which astronomers can pick up with radio telescopes today. This 'microwave background radiation' is one of our best pieces of evidence that the Big Bang did really happen as theory describes.

Another piece of evidence comes from the proportion of different gases that we find in the Universe now. The Big Bang should have produced hydrogen, the simplest of all the elements. When the Universe was three minutes old, some of the hydrogen should have reacted to form the next element, helium. Indeed, there are gas clouds in the Universe today that do have exactly the proportion of hydrogen and helium that the Big Bang theory predicts.

So, the early expanding Universe was filled with swirling clouds of hydrogen and helium. We might expect that this gas just spread out and filled space in a uniform way to create a lifeless Universe, for ever consisting simply of tenuous gas. But gravity decreed that this was not to be: the gas would clump together to form galaxies, stars, planets – and, eventually, life.

In the first fraction of a second after its birth, the Universe expanded immensely in size. Astronomers believe that this Big Bang took place in two distinct stages.

In this sequence of images of the early Universe, each successive step lasts for only the briefest moment: to be precise, a million-million-million-million-million-millionth of a second.

First, a small searingly hot ball of matter appears from nothing. At the beginning it is smaller than an atom, but it contains all of space and time. Its matter is very compressed, but it weighs no more than a couple of kilograms. For a few moments, the ball – and space with it – expands at a fairly gradual pace.

But this ball is made of substances that can exist only at immensely high temperatures. As it expands, the ball cools down until its original matter is unstable. After a few moments – in the middle of this sequence – it starts to turn into the kind of matter and forces that we have today.

According to the most widely accepted theory, the change of one kind of matter into another produces an immense explosion. In another moment of time, the Universe expands from the size of an atom to something larger than the Earth. During this moment of inflation, the Universe creates all the matter that later makes up the galaxies and stars. And the momentum from the explosion keeps the matter of the Universe flying apart, right up to the present day.

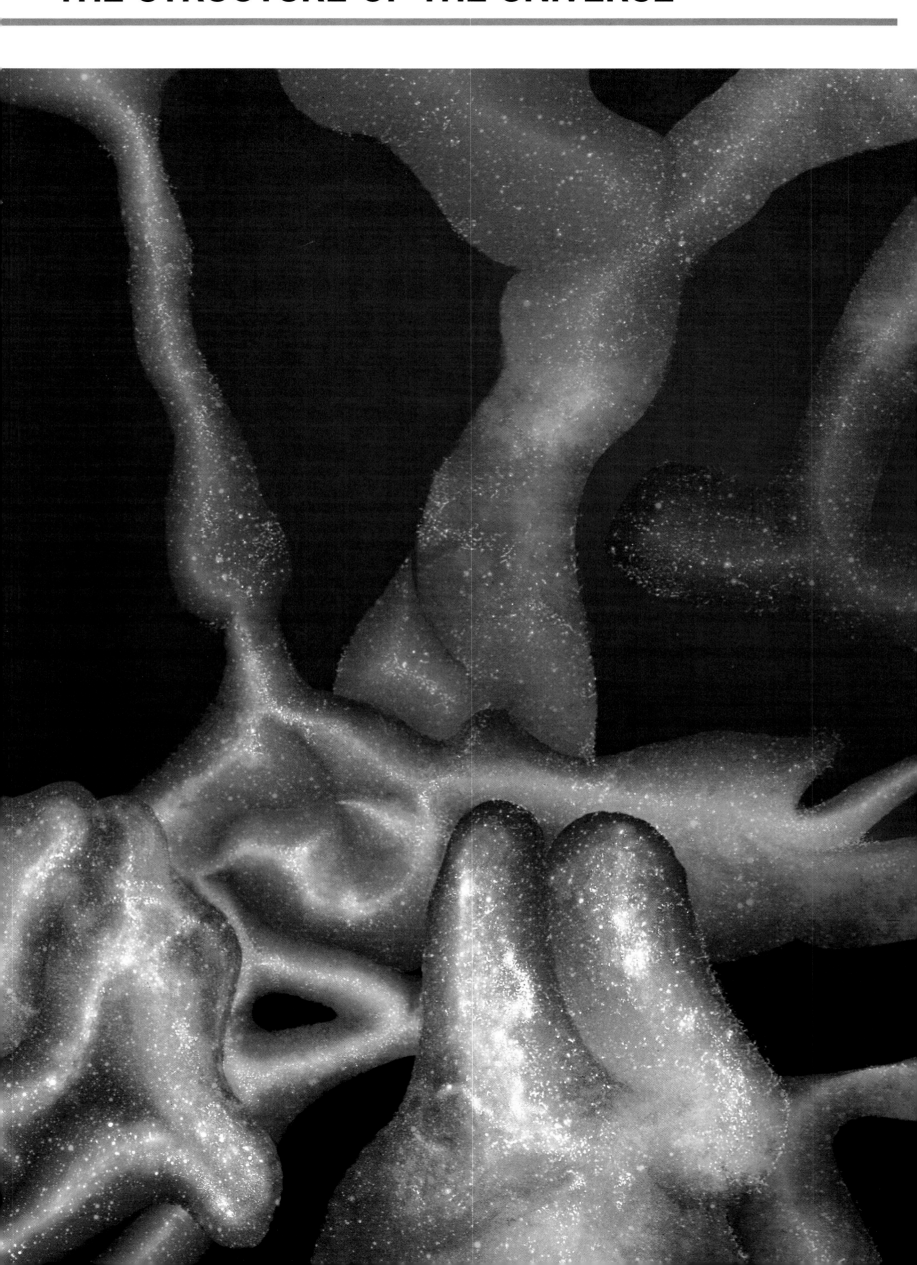

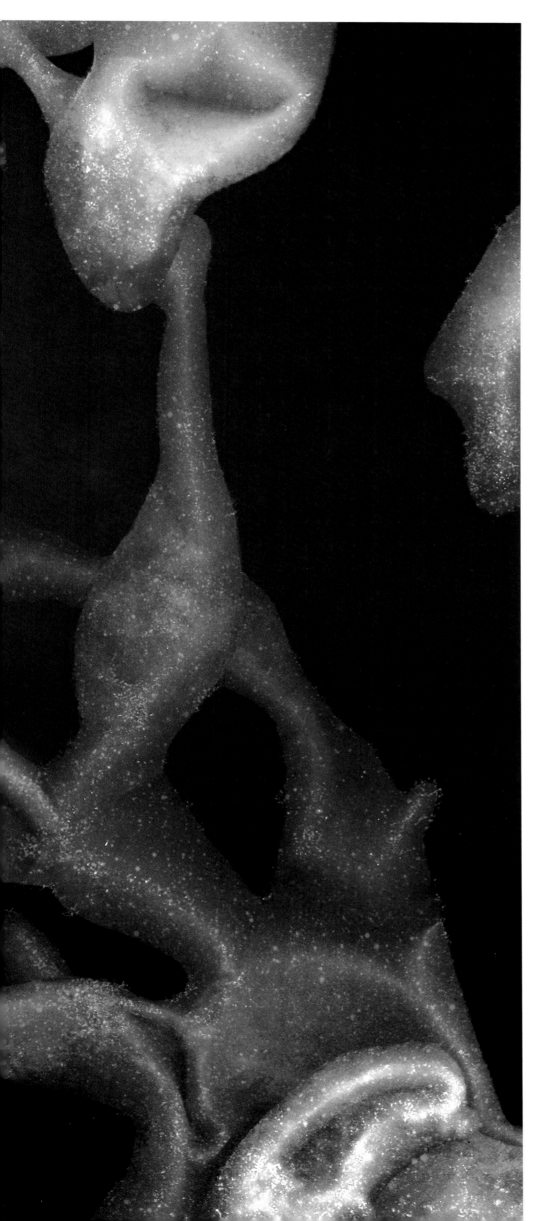

After the Big Bang, the Universe was full of swirling hot gases, together with radiation and perhaps other – as yet unknown – ingredients. As the Universe grew in age and size, the gas expanded to fill the new space that was for ever being created. The material of the Universe began to cool, and eventually, like a cosmic cheese, it 'curdled'.

The gas did not clump together at random. It avoided certain regions, to leave empty holes. As the Universe has expanded, some of these holes have grown to become over 200 million light years across, where a light year is about 10 million million kilometres.

The gas became concentrated into walls that separated the holes, and at the join of two walls it formed long filaments: to use another food analogy, it congealed into long, spaghetti-like strands. The gas in the strands eventually broke up into individual galaxies, like the Milky Way Galaxy that we live in.

Astronomers cannot actually see the filaments that looped round the early Universe, but they are fairly confident that the gas did condense in this way. In the past few years, they have discovered that the galaxies we see near us today are arranged in long filaments that must trace out an ancient pattern of gas. Walls seem to repeat roughly every 400 million light years through space, while an individual enormous filament of galaxies in the direction of the constellations Perseus and Pegasus stretches over 1,000 million light years.

Certain theories of the Universe actually lead naturally to the appearance of holes, walls and filaments in the early Universe. In the 1930s, the German astronomer Fritz Zwicky suggested that most of the matter in the Universe is not in the form of the stars and galaxies that we see, but is dark and totally invisible. In the past few years, most astronomers have come to agree with Zwicky. One popular idea is that the 'dark matter' consists of a vast sea of subatomic particles, filling the whole Universe.

Although these dark particles – with names like axions, neutrinos and photinos – do not have much to do with the ordinary matter that makes galaxies, stars and us, they do exert a gravitational pull. When astronomers used computers to recalculate what happened after the Big Bang if the gas was permeated by dark matter, they found that it would naturally condense into the 'spaghetti' shown here – just the kind of structure that would lead to the distribution of galaxies that we find in the Universe today.

A million years after the Big Bang, the gas in the Universe has condensed into long filaments, or 'spaghetti'. Each filament is hundreds of millions of light years long.

This image is based on a computer simulation of how matter should 'curdle' after the Big Bang, if ordinary matter is mixed with a much larger amount of invisible 'dark matter'. American astronomers Joan Centrella and Adrian Melott used a supercomputer to calculate the shape of these gaseous structures in the early Universe.

This gas will eventually break up into individual galaxies, lying in long strings that are separated by large empty holes. The result shown here reproduces well the actual distribution of galaxies in the Universe today: our own Galaxy, for example, is about one-third of the way along a filament of galaxies, the centre of which is marked by a giant cluster of galaxies in the constellation Virgo.

GALAXIES START TO FORM

The episode of the Universe's history that we understand least is not the earliest part – the gas and radiation left over from the original Big Bang have revealed much about it – but the second stage of the story. This is when gravity marshalled the dilute gases from the Big Bang into stars and galaxies.

Today, the visible Universe consists mainly of stars – each very much like the Sun – bunched together into galaxies. (There may also be a great deal of dark matter, which we cannot see.) Galaxies are vast agglomerations of stars: even the 'dwarf' galaxies contain over a million stars, and some galaxies consist of over a million million stars. Many galaxies also contain clouds of gas and dust.

The Sun is one of the 200,000 million stars that make up a moderately large galaxy, the Milky Way. The myriad stars of the Milky Way are spread across our sky as a pale glowing band of light, which the ancient Greeks believed to be milk spilt from the breast of the goddess Hera. From the Greek word for 'milk' we have the alternative name 'Galaxy' for the Milky Way. Astronomers use the word 'galaxy' for the other star-islands in the Universe, too.

Galaxies are in groups or larger clusters in space. Some of these clusters may contain thousands of individual galaxies. The clusters, in turn, make up 'superclusters', and these form the building blocks of the vast walls and filaments that fill the Universe.

Consisting more of glowing gas clouds than stars, a galaxy begins to condense out of the matter left over from the Big Bang. This 'proto-galaxy' has formed from a lump of gas that was swirling fast enough to flatten itself into a disc: in time, it will form spiral arms, as we see in the newly born galaxy immediately behind the proto-galaxy.

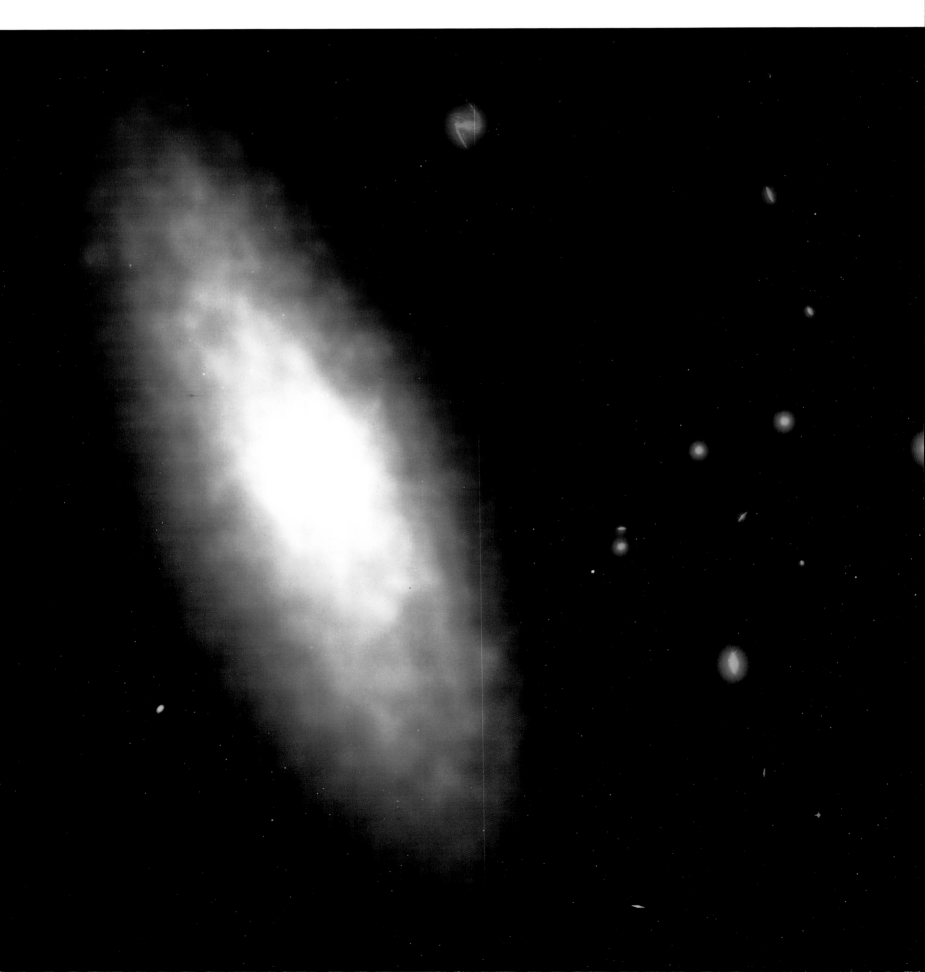

When it comes to the origin of the galaxies, astronomers are very much in the position of wondering whether the chicken or the egg came first. The Soviet scientist Yakov Zel'dovich has suggested that the gases from the Big Bang first formed into the enormous walls and filaments. Individual clumps of gas in these structures broke into smaller and smaller pieces – the size of superclusters and then clusters – and finally into galaxy-sized gas blobs that actually condensed into individual galaxies of stars.

Some American astronomers hold an entirely opposing view. They believe that the original material condensed into a huge number of very small blobs of gas, each of which became a star (or a small group of stars), spread more-or-less evenly throughout the Universe. The gravity of these stars attracted them to each other, so they grouped in galaxies. The galaxies then banded together in clusters and superclusters.

Astronomers have worked out in detail one version of this second theory, as shown here. Clumps of gas about a thousand light years across coagulate out of the original gas from the Big Bang. Some of these clumps form into individual small galaxies, while others gather together in their hundreds to build up larger galaxies, like our Milky Way.

As the small gas clouds jostle in the outer regions of what would become the eventual galaxy, some of the gas was compressed and immediately turned to stars. The stars of this 'first generation' will, for ever afterwards, pursue large orbits in the outer regions of the galaxy.

Like two planes colliding in mid-air and falling to Earth, the collisions between the small gas clouds slowed down their motions around the embryonic galaxy, and they gradually fell in towards the centre. As the gas accumulated in the middle of the 'proto-galaxy',

more and more of it turned into stars. These bright young stars lit up the gas around them, so that the whole proto-galaxy was brilliant with the fluorescent blue light of hot stars and crimson-red radiation from the surrounding hot gas. At this stage, a galaxy like our Milky Way was almost a hundred times brighter than it is now.

According to this theory, most of the large galaxies were born in the first 1,000 million years after the Big Bang – when the Universe was less than one-tenth of its present age. We can check out this idea on our Milky Way Galaxy. Just as an archaeologist can tell when people first occupied a site by the age of the earliest pieces of pottery found there, so astronomers can date a galaxy's birth from the age of its oldest stars. In our Galaxy, stars are being born all the time, so they cover a great range in ages. But the most ancient stars are all about 14,000 million years old: they – and the Galaxy as a whole – were indeed born some 1,000 million years after the Big Bang.

In the 1980s and 1990s, astronomers have been peering ever deeper into the Universe – and further back in time – to try to see galaxies being born during the dawn of our Universe. They may have found a few objects that are probably proto-galaxies, but not as many as they expected.

To their surprise, these cosmic archaeologists have, however, found many smaller galaxies that formed billions of years later in the history of the Universe. Although the most massive galaxies were almost certainly born soon after the Big Bang, it now seems that many of their smaller siblings appeared well afterwards. Indeed, some small bright gas clouds in space, relatively near the Milky Way, are probably the latest generation of dwarf galaxies, only now condensing from primeval gas.

1.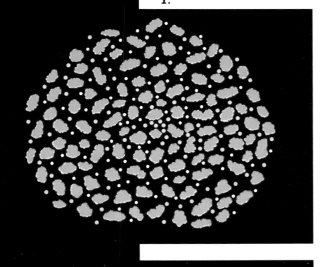

2.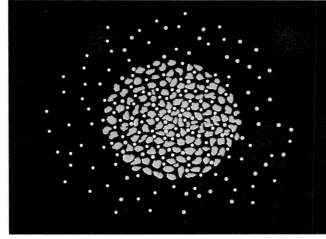

 3.

4.

1. *According to computer calculations, a galaxy begins to form when small gas clouds come together. Collisions between the clouds produce a scattering of stars, stretching over some 200,000 light years of space.*

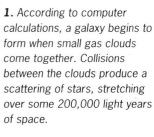

2. *After 200 million years, the clouds have collapsed to a smaller size, leaving the original stars as a large halo around the central proto-galaxy, which is about 100,000 light years across.*

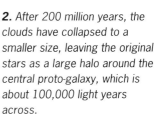

3. *Another 200 million years on, and the gas clouds are so compressed that they are forming stars at an immense rate. The proto-galaxy is now at its maximum brightness.*

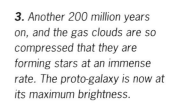

4. *After another 200 million years, most of the gas has turned into stars. These stars, and the remaining gas, form a striking spiral shape in the galaxy's disc. Surrounding the disc are the now-faint stars of the galaxy's halo.*

QUASARS

When the Universe was young, gas clouds crashed together to form new galaxies, incandescent nebulae shone red and infra-red, young massive stars blazed forth in ultra-violet splendour. But these examples of cosmic violence are as nothing when compared to the quasars.

A quasar is the most intense concentration of energy in the Universe. It shines with the light of a hundred galaxies, but is no larger than our Solar System. To put that into perspective, imagine representing an ordinary galaxy – like our Milky Way – by a standard household light bulb. Then a quasar is a light bulb that is as brilliant as a searchlight, but no larger than an atom.

The scientists who first discovered quasars were radio astronomers. From the late 1940s onwards, they found hundreds of natural radio 'broadcasters' in the sky. Many of these turned out to be distant galaxies that were extremely powerful natural broadcasters of radio waves. In 1962, radio astronomers pinned down precisely the position of a radio source known as '3C 273' (the 273rd entry in the third Cambridge catalogue of radio sources). Photographs showed that this looked like a star – but with a 'jet' (a thin wisp of light) emerging from one side of it.

A Dutch-American astronomer, Maarten Schmidt, analyzed the light from 3C 273, and found it was moving away from us at a tremendous speed, far faster than anything in our Galaxy. Schmidt deduced that 3C 273 was actually very distant – about 2,000 million light years away – and was being carried away from us at high speed by the expansion of the Universe. For such a remote object to shine so brightly in our skies, 3C 273 had to be much brighter than a galaxy, even though it was clearly much smaller. Astronomers quickly located more of these 'quasi-stellar radio sources' – a term soon shortened to 'quasars'.

A few astronomers have disputed Schmidt's interpretation of the light from the quasars, and believe that they are dimmer objects lying much closer to the Milky Way. Most astronomers now accept, however, that quasars are extremely distant. The clinching evidence has been pictures of quasars taken with sensitive electronic cameras on the world's largest telescopes. On these pictures, we can see that the quasar itself lies in the middle of a much fainter galaxy. In fact, these galaxies are quite normal: our view of them is overwhelmed by the brilliance of the quasar in the centre. These galaxies are indeed very distant, confirming that the quasars inside them are also very remote, and must therefore be extremely powerful.

As astronomers have located more and more quasars, they have found that there are only a few quasars near to us, and many more as we look at regions further and further away. Does this mean that we live in a region of space uninhabited by quasars? Probably not – because we need to bear in mind that, as we look into space, we are looking back in time. We see even the nearest quasar, 3C 273, as it was 2,000 million years ago. The light from the most distant – and most plentiful – quasars left them when the Universe was only one-tenth of its present age. So quasars are outbreaks of violence that disturbed the centre of many galaxies when the Universe was young.

Astronomers have devised the following theory to explain not only what a quasar is, but why a quasar outburst was a symptom of a galaxy's youth.

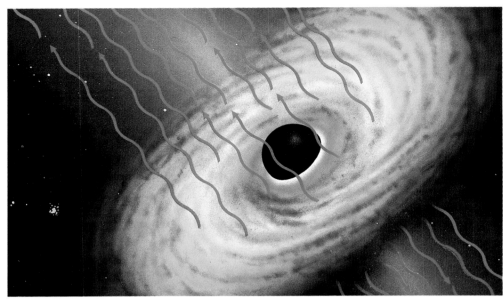

When a galaxy was born out of the gas left over from the Big Bang, some of the gas fell towards the galaxy's centre. The heart of the galaxy soon contained an immense amount of gas – as much as 1,000 million Suns – heaped together within a very small space. The gravity of this heap of gas was so strong that nothing – not even light – could escape: it was a black hole. A black hole is a region of space where matter is squeezed together so powerfully that its gravity is irresistible: light cannot escape, so it appears 'black'; nothing that falls in can ever get out again, so it is the ultimate 'hole'.

A black hole itself could not be a quasar, because no light can escape from inside the hole. But these black holes lay in the centres of young galaxies, and in these early days there was plenty of spare gas around the galaxy. The black hole's gravity could attract this gas, and draw it in. In addition, stars straying too close to the hole were torn apart into strands of gas that also fell towards the black hole. Astronomers have calculated that the gas did not fall straight into the hole, but whirled around in a spiral. The spiralling gas formed a disc about the size of the Solar System. The black hole's gravity squeezed the gas in the surrounding disc until it was so hot that it shone brilliantly – emitting copious amounts of light and other radiation. The disc became a quasar.

The swirling gases in the quasar disc also acted as an electrical generator, producing streams of electric current that shot off into space on either side of the disc itself. We can see one of these streams of electricity as the jet of light extending from 3C 273. These giant electrical currents produce strong radio waves, and radio telescopes show large jets extending from many quasars. The powerful 'radio galaxies' discovered before quasars contain black holes that generate powerful electrical jets but have a much fainter central disc.

As time went by, the black hole scooped up all the spare gas and stars in the galaxy's centre. The gas in the quasar disc all spiralled into the black hole and disappeared. The galaxy's centre now became dim; as its supply of gas dried up, the quasar flickered and went out.

That is why quasars were so abundant when the Universe was young but are so rare at the present time. But we can expect to find, in the centre of many galaxies – possibly including our own – a 'dead' quasar: a massive black hole.

Above: Clouds of cool gas, shining with the pale pink light from hydrogen, form a reservoir that keeps the brilliant quasar disc topped up with matter.

The hot spinning disc acts as an electrical generator, shooting electric currents off into space on either side. These beams of electricity (shown as blue arrows) can extend a million light years into space.

Right: The heart of a quasar is a brilliant swirl of gases disappearing down a massive black hole.

The black hole in the centre contains over a billion times more matter than the Sun. This matter is compressed so much that its gravity is irresistible: not even light can escape its pull, so the hole appears absolutely dark.

The black hole lies in the middle of a young galaxy, and its strong gravity pulls in the gas that has been left over from the galaxy's birth – and the remnants of any stars that have ventured too close to the black hole, and have been ripped apart by its immense pull.

All this gas forms a vortex around the black hole, like bath water going down the drain. The swirling gas becomes hotter and hotter as it approaches the black hole itself, and glows more and more brightly. Just before it disappears into the hole, the gas emits a brilliant burst of radiation, including ultra-violet and X-rays as well as ordinary light.

The bright disc that makes up the quasar is no larger than the Solar System, yet it can shine with the brightness of a hundred galaxies.

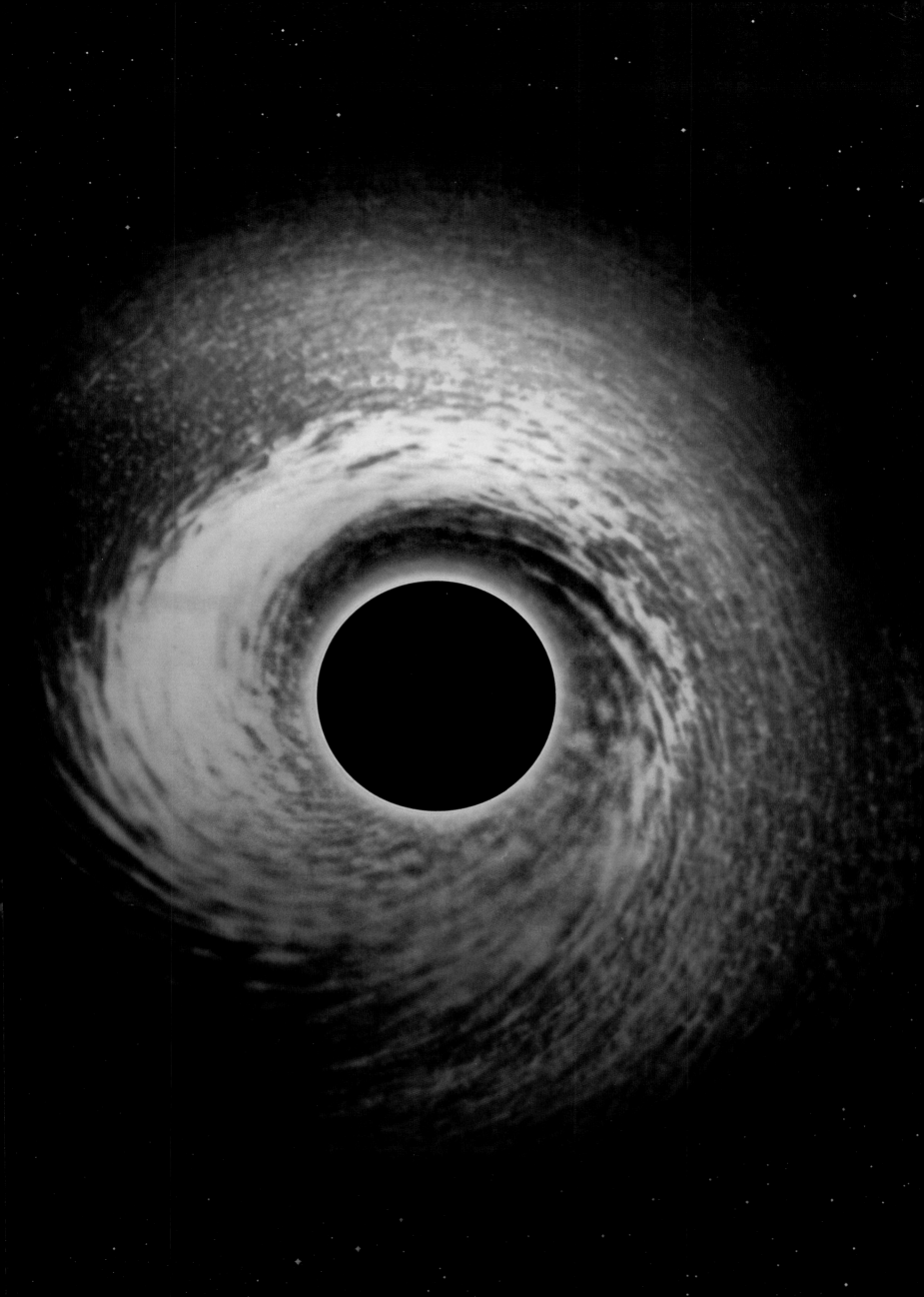

EXPANDING GALAXIES

Until recent years, astronomers thought that galaxies have remained the same since they were born. But now there is strong evidence that some galaxies have grown vastly bigger since their birth. A growing galaxy must have something to feed on. A typical galaxy such as our Milky Way has no obvious source of nourishment around: it floats in virtually empty intergalactic space. There are regions of the Universe, however, where a galaxy does have a supply of food to hand: within clusters of galaxies.

Astronomers have known that galaxies are not spread out uniformly through space since the pioneering work of the German astronomer Max Wolf a century ago. Using the contemporary term for galaxies, he described how he had come across 'nests of nebulae'. In the 1950s, the American astronomer George Abell drew up a catalogue of 2,712 clusters of galaxies. Looking far out into space, we see the most distant clusters of galaxies as they were shortly after the Big Bang.

Most of the galaxies within a cluster are moving about at high speed, but they cannot escape because they are restrained by the gravitational pull of all the other galaxies. The combined gravity from the galaxies can also hold on to atoms of gas, keeping them in a giant 'pool' that fills the cluster of galaxies. Some of this gas is left over from the Big Bang; some has come from exploding stars (supernovae) within the galaxies.

When the original gas fell into the cluster, it became extremely hot – reaching an almost unbelievable 100 million degrees C. We cannot see this superhot gas with any ordinary telescope, but it is a powerful source of natural X-rays. Special satellites have picked up radiation from many distant clusters of galaxies, confirming that they do indeed contain vast pools of superheated gas. The gas is so tenuous, however, that it could not heat up a galaxy's stars to these disruptingly high temperatures.

Despite its high temperature, such tenuous gas has problems in losing its heat and cooling down. The gas can actually cool most efficiently in regions where it is densest – that is, in the very centre of the cluster of galaxies.

A British astronomer, Andy Fabian, has calculated how long it would take for the central regions of gas to cool down to everyday temperatures. In some clusters, the superhot gases from the birth of the cluster should still be at a temperature around 100 million degrees C. But in many cases, the gas in the centre of the cluster should have cooled right down by now.

The problem is this. Originally, the gas in the centre of the cluster was being squeezed by the hot surrounding gas and, when it cooled down, the central gas was not able to fight back: the pressure should then have squeezed the central gas right down into a very small and cold gas cloud. This kind of gas should emit distinctive radiation, in the form of light or radio waves – yet telescopes do not pick up either of these kinds of radiation.

Fabian points out that the centre of these clusters often contains a large elliptical galaxy. Elliptical galaxies usually have little or no glowing gas in their vicinity, but these particular examples are sometimes fringed by faint wisps of glowing gas. He proposes that the wisps are actually the 'cooling flows' of the colder denser gas being forced into the central galaxy.

The ultimate fate of this gas, Fabian believes, is to turn into stars. These add to the complement of stars already making up the elliptical galaxy. His calculations have produced a result that has startled astronomers, and is still controversial. Since the gas began to cool, billions of years ago, enough matter has flowed into the central galaxy to make up most of the stars that the galaxy now contains. In other words, immediately after the Big Bang, the central galaxy was considerably smaller than it is now. By steadily consuming the gas around it, the galaxy has been able to produce more and more stars to add to its bulk, until it has grown to several times its original size.

Right: Immense streamers of glowing red gas fall into a galaxy from space. The gas condenses into a multitude of new stars, building up a small collection of stars into a mammoth galaxy.

1. A small galaxy is surrounded by a huge cloud of hot gas. At a temperature of over 100 million degrees C, this gas is invisible to ordinary telescopes.

2. After 500 million years, the central part of the hot gas cloud has begun to cool. When it reaches a temperature of 10,000°C, the gas begins to glow red, and starts to drizzle inwards towards the galaxy.

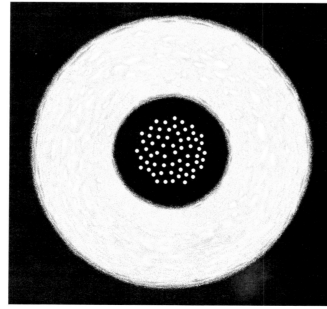

1.

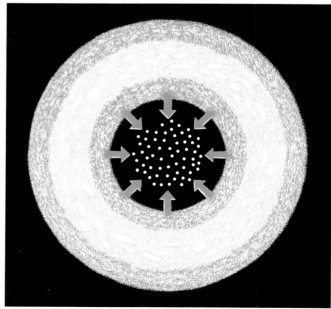

2.

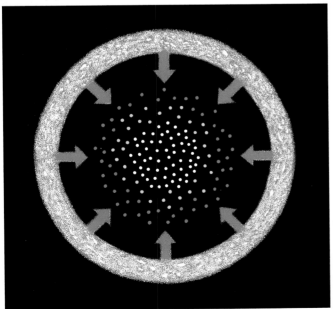

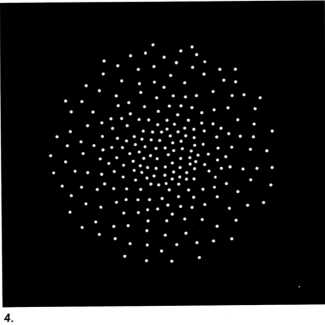

3. Another 500 million years on, and the inflowing gas has turned into stars that are increasing the galaxy's bulk. More of the hot gas is now cooling down, and raining down on the galaxy.

4. With the passing of the next 1,000 million years, the entire gas cloud has cooled, and all its matter has flowed into the galaxy. The infalling gas has made so many new stars that the galaxy now ranks with the largest and most massive that we know.

3.

4.

DIFFERENT KINDS OF GALAXY

In the first 1,000 million years after the Big Bang, the hot gases condensed into a multitude of star-islands. These galaxies were far from being look-alikes, and they have retained their individuality to this day: astronomers recognize a wide range of galaxies and can unerringly put a name to some of the most familiar of them.

Broadly speaking, the primordial gases formed into two kinds of galaxy. The first type consisted *only* of stars, while the second type had a good measure of gas and dust lying between the stars. We see both kinds of galaxy around us today, and astronomers have sifted them for clues as to how they were born and how they came to have their distinctive shapes.

Most galaxies contain only the amount of matter that they were born with – but this covers a huge range. Our Milky Way, with 200,000 million stars, is rather larger than average. The biggest of all, the giant ellipticals, are made up of several million million stars. At the other end of the range are dwarf galaxies that contain only a million stars – no more than some clusters of stars within our Milky Way.

The type of galaxy – and hence the way that it looks now – was governed not by the amount of matter around at its birth, but by the amount of rotation in the gas. Each clump (or bunch of clumps) from the Big Bang must have been spinning to a certain extent, just as everything in the Universe now is rotating – from galaxies down to planets.

If a clump was spinning only very slowly, the rotation had little effect on its birth. Gravity simply pulled the gas towards the centre, compressing it so much that all the gas turned into stars almost at once. These stars formed a swarm with a shape that was roughly spherical: it might be slightly flattened, or elongated, depending on the shape of the original clump. An elliptical galaxy had been born.

An elliptical galaxy is simply a swarm of stars, milling around in a crowd that is held together by the gravity of all the stars pulling on one another. Astronomers are interested in them because they are fossils of the early Universe, consisting entirely of old stars – the first generation of stars formed soon after the Big Bang.

Something much more spectacular was in store, however, if a clump of gas from the Big Bang was spinning. Gravity started pulling the gases in the clump inwards, to form a first generation of stars in a spherical volume of space. But as the remaining gas fell towards the centre, it rotated faster and faster – just as an ice skater spins faster by drawing in his or her arms. Centrifugal force then prevented this whirling gas from falling to the galaxy's centre. Instead, the gas formed a flat disc.

In the disc, centrifugal force continued to provide a balance to gravity, so the gas was never compressed enough to form stars all at once. Over the aeons, some of the gas gradually turned to stars, but at least one-tenth of the galaxy's matter remained in the form of gas. This thinly spread material between the stars was partly the remains of the original gas, but it also contained gas and tiny solid particles of 'dust' ejected by stars that were living and dying.

When a gas-filled galaxy contained only a small amount of matter – less than 1,000 million stars – it acquired no particular shape. Such galaxies consist, to this day, of a clutter of stars of different ages and clouds of gas and dust, and astronomers disparagingly refer to them as 'irregular galaxies'.

If a gas-filled galaxy was relatively heavy, however, something almost miraculous occurred. The stars and gas in its disc heaped themselves together to make a spiral pattern. These spiral galaxies are among the most beautiful and intricate natural objects in the Universe. The shape of the spiral pattern differs from one to another, so astronomers can often recognize

Due to accidents of birth, and the vicissitudes of life, galaxies exist in a wide range of shapes and sizes.

__1.__ A dwarf elliptical is one of the smallest kinds of galaxy. It consists of only about a million stars arranged in an oval shape, with no gas or dust between the stars.

__2.__ A giant elliptical is the largest type of galaxy. It is a roughly spherical ball of over a million million stars, with no gas or dust. This galaxy is 500,000 light years across. To give an idea of the galaxy's scale, each of the faint blobs around its edge is a cluster consisting of a million stars.

__3.__ This giant galaxy has collided with a spiral galaxy, which has bequeathed it a dark band of dust and gas. Some of this matter is falling on to a black hole at the galaxy's centre, and refuelling a sleeping quasar there.

__4.__ An irregular galaxy. As well as stars, it contains a large amount of gas, shining pink, and dark dust patches. This material is gradually turning into new stars.

__5.__ The most beautiful galaxies are the spirals. The yellowish glow in the centre consists of old stars, and this region resembles a small elliptical galaxy. Surrounding this hub is a flat disc, made up of stars, gas and dust. The material in the disc is marshalled into distinctive spiral arms, with shapes that are individual to each spiral galaxy.

__6.__ In a spiral galaxy viewed at an angle, we can see how the matter outside the hub is laid out in a flat disc. The dust shows up clearly as it hides many of the galaxy's stars.

__7.__ This is a galaxy somewhere between an irregular and a spiral, classed by astronomers as a 'one-armed spiral'.

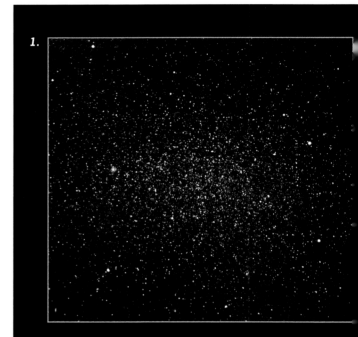

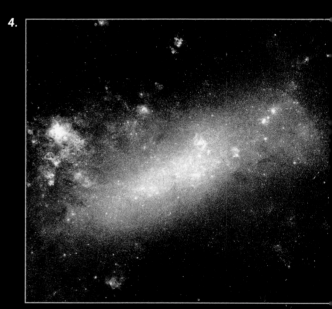

an individual spiral galaxy by name, at a glance. The nearby Andromeda Galaxy is one well-known example; another is our Milky Way, though we cannot actually see its spiral shape because we live inside it.

Although spiral galaxies are so common and so familiar, astronomers cannot agree on why their matter takes up this striking shape. According to one theory, some disturbance – such as the gravity of a passing galaxy – pulls the matter into a spiral, and the spiral shape itself has enough gravitational pull to hold stars and gas within its limits, and so perpetuate the pattern traced by this matter. Another theory suggests that supernovae compress the matter in the galaxy's disc into bunches of gas and young stars, and the rotation of the galaxy stretches these bunches of gas and stars out into spiral arms, in almost exactly the same way as you can make a spiral pattern by stirring cream into a cup of coffee.

3.

CLOSE ENCOUNTERS BETWEEN GALAXIES

In the Universe today, galaxies usually drift past one another like ships in the night, missing each other by large distances. But when the Universe was young, close encounters were the rule rather than the exception. The galaxies were about the same size as they are today, but the Universe itself was a much smaller place, and the galaxies were jostling for elbow-room.

Astronomers believe that such encounters could have changed the course of a young galaxy's life. So, understanding the effects of collisions is an important part of disentangling the history of the galaxies. Computers have been essential to astronomers involved in this forensic science of the cosmos. A computer can take account of the fact that a galaxy is not a single connected object, like a planet. It is a loose collection of billions of stars, held together only by the invisible bonds of gravity.

When a galaxy 'collides' with another, there is no physical smash-up of the kind we get when an asteroid hits the Earth. The stars of one galaxy pass by the stars of the other, like two swarms of gnats flying through one another. But the stars in one galaxy pull on the gravitational threads holding the other together, with strange – and often beautiful – effects.

In 1972, two brothers working in the United States, Alar and Juri Toomre, first used a computer to 'collide' two galaxies. At that time, most astronomers expected that the result would simply be a stretching of the galaxies. To the Toomres' surprise, the galaxies in the computer instead pulled off long thin ribbons of stars from one another.

Immediately, the brothers realized that close encounters of this kind could cause some of the odd galaxies that we see in the Universe today. These are distinguished by long streamers, or 'tails', which had led to descriptive names like the Antennae and The Mice. These must be rare examples of galaxies that are having a close brush at the present time.

Many astronomers have now extended and refined this computer technique. They simulate many kinds of encounters until they reach a final outcome that resembles a pair of interacting galaxies we have

1. A small flat galaxy sails dangerously close to the edge of a larger galaxy. The following sequence shows what happens next in this close encounter of a galactic kind, according to calculations by the French astronomer Françoise Combes.

2. As the galaxies begin to separate, 100 million years later, the gravitational pull of the small galaxy has clearly disturbed the paths of the stars in the outer parts of the larger galaxy.

4. *After another interval of 100 million years, we see narrow streamers of stars that have been flung out into space from both galaxies. Many of these stars will be lost for ever to their parent galaxies.*

3. *Another 100 million years on, and the outer parts of both galaxies have now been seriously disrupted by the gravity of the other. Gas clouds in the galaxies' centres have also been churned up, and are producing a sudden rash of new stars.*

actually photographed. The computer sequence leading to this outcome thus tells us the history of that particular encounter.

In any encounter, the gravitational pull generally rips away some of the outermost stars. These stars are lost into intergalactic space and each galaxy ends up smaller. But close encounters can have other, more unexpected, effects. A neighbour that makes a near miss can, for example, stir up the gas in a galaxy in such a way that it intensifies the pattern of spiral arms.

Astronomers believe that many galaxies contain a massive black hole that is a dead quasar – starved of surrounding gas. If another galaxy passes nearby, it can disturb the motion of gas clouds in the galaxy and

send them on a collision course with a black hole. As the gases reach it, the black hole sweeps them into a swirling disc that is as brilliant as a hundred galaxies: the quasar is briefly rekindled.

When a small galaxy dives straight through the middle of a large spiral one, the shock of its passage pushes the gas in the larger galaxy outwards, so it piles up around the edge. This compressed gas shines brightly with newly formed stars and nebulae. It forms an incandescent ring around a much dimmer central region – a sight that astronomers call a 'cartwheel galaxy'.

Any two galaxies making a close pass can perturb each other's gases enough to generate the formation of new stars in one another. Sometimes, however, they collide head-on and produce an exceptionally intense blaze of star birth. This phenomenon – a starburst galaxy – is one of the most powerful in the known Universe, second only to the quasars in its output of energy. In these cases, the galaxies usually stay entangled with one another, and eventually become a single normal galaxy.

Because galaxy encounters must have been much more common in the early days of the Universe, astronomers believe that many of the young galaxies must have collided – or at least had a serious encounter – with another youthful galaxy. As a result, we can be fairly sure that many of those we see around us today are the relics of cosmic collisions in the early Universe.

GALACTIC CANNIBALISM

The most immense galaxies in the Universe have grown to their current bulk by consuming smaller galaxies. Because these monsters are always oval in shape, astronomers call them 'supergiant elliptical galaxies'. This term describes 'cannibals' that have grown fat on stars accumulated from the galaxies that they have devoured.

We find these enormous galaxies only in the centre of clusters of galaxies. The most massive specimens consist of 100 million million stars – hundreds of times more than the Milky Way contains. A supergiant elliptical can stretch over a million light years of space. A sprinkling of stars even further out forms a vast faint 'halo' around the galaxy itself – something that is unique to these galaxies.

The supergiant elliptical stays stationary in the centre of the cluster, like a spider in its web, as the other galaxies swarm around. Occasionally, one of the smaller ones will find itself on a collision course with the giant elliptical.

At first, the collision does not seem to bring about ruin. The stars in a galaxy are so well separated that the stars in the two galaxies do not actually hit one another. The momentum of the small galaxy carries it through the supergiant almost unscathed: the supergiant has merely robbed it of a few of its outermost stars.

But the gravity of the supergiant puts the brakes on the small galaxy. After passing through the larger galaxy, it is moving so slowly that it cannot get away completely. The gravity of the supergiant elliptical brings the escaping galaxy to a halt, and pulls it back to collide again. The second encounter robs the smaller galaxy of more energy. After passing through the supergiant, it is attracted back even sooner than before. It bobs back and forth through the supergiant, becoming more and more ensnared in the larger galaxy's gravity.

Each time the small galaxy passes through, the supergiant elliptical strips more stars from its outer regions. The fate of the trapped galaxy is now sealed. Inexorably, its stars are stripped away and added to the supergiant's vast bulk. Some of the newly acquired stars are flung about so fast that they end up outside the main body of the giant galaxy, to form the faint halo of stars that surround it.

In most galaxies – whether elliptical or spiral – the stars near the centre are so closely packed that they form a distinctive bright patch of light, or core, at its heart. About one-quarter of the supergiant ellipticals, however, have more than one core of stars. The brightest core is the actual centre of the huge galaxy, while the others are the centres of smaller ones that are in the process of being consumed.

The record holder is a supergiant elliptical in the constellation Hercules, known as 'NGC 6166' (from its position in the New General Catalogue of nebulae and galaxies). It lies right in the middle of a cluster that contains thousands of smaller galaxies. Photographs show that it is currently devouring a pair of small galaxies from its entourage: they are visible now only as two extra cores within the supergiant. Hints of another core suggest that it has just finished devouring another galaxy. As a result of its cannibalism, NGC 6166 has grown from a fairly normal galaxy to become one of the largest that we know in the Universe.

A huge 'cannibal' galaxy has built up its bulk by feeding on smaller companions. The galaxy's bright core consists of the stars of a dozen galaxies it has swallowed in the remote past.

The other concentrations of stars within the galaxy are the cores of galaxies that have been consumed more recently: the cannibal has absorbed their outlying stars, but it will take longer to digest the cores.

A medium-sized elliptical galaxy is the next victim, already in the gravitational snare of the cannibal. It has passed once through the fringes of the giant galaxy, and cannot now escape.

The small spiral is now approaching the giant galaxy for the first time. It may sail by safely on this occasion, but ultimately it will fall prey to the cosmic cannibal.

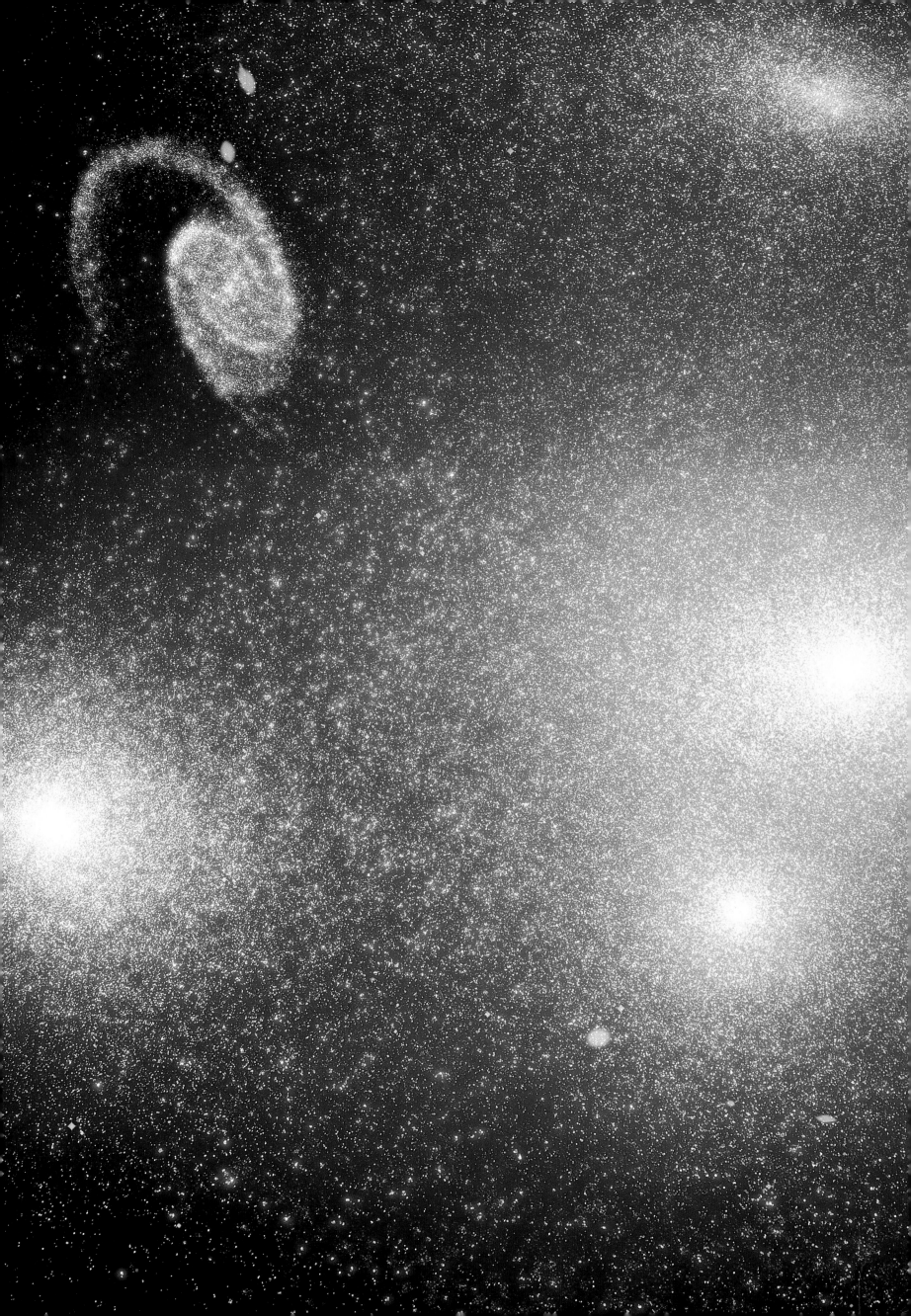

THE MIDDLE DISTANCE

10 billion to 5 billion years ago

The middle period in the life of the Universe began long after the excitement of the Big Bang had died down. In fact, all the fireworks of the early Universe were starting to fade. The quasars in the centres of galaxies were, in the main, fizzling out. Collisions between galaxies were becoming rarer as the expansion of the Universe drew the galaxies further apart. Some galaxies were still growing fatter as they fed on gas flowing in from space or consumed their neighbours, but on the whole the galaxies – or at least the larger ones, like our Milky Way – had reached more or less their eventual size and shape.

Attention now turns to what was going on inside the galaxies. The elliptical galaxies were already cosmic graveyards: they had converted all their original gas into stars in one sudden burst of activity, and those stars were now old and dying.

The beautiful spiral galaxies, however, set up a scheme of cosmic recycling that enabled them to preserve their youth for billions of years. When a spiral galaxy was born from primeval gases, only nine-tenths of this matter condensed into stars. The rest was left as tenuous wraiths of gas between the stars, mainly out in the galaxy's gaudy spiral-shaped arms. As aeons passed, some of this gas condensed into fresh generations of bright young stars, so keeping the galaxy – at least in the spiral arms – appearing young and vigorous.

Just as important, when these stars eventually died, they flung a great deal of their matter back into space. This bequest of gas from dying stars became mixed up with the existing gas in space, to replenish the reservoir of gases that was available to condense into the next generation of stars.

This was recycling on the grandest scale: the recovery of matter from dying stars to create more stars. But this is not all. The ashes from a dying star are rich with new chemical elements that have been made with the star during its life. These new and exotic substances enrich the gas between the stars, which started out containing only hydrogen and helium. In addition, some stars go out in a spectacular way, blowing themselves apart in a supernova explosion. The shock waves from a supernova can squeeze the surrounding gases and so trigger the birth of new stars. A star is a celestial phoenix: from the ashes of a dying star can rise a whole new generation of stars.

We are treated to some stunning views of star birth, bright young stars and star death because we live in a spiral galaxy. The Milky Way Galaxy provides an ideal site for cosmic archaeologists to delve into the history of a typical spiral galaxy, where we can investigate in detail the cycles of star life that kept our Galaxy alive and vibrant through the middle ages of the Universe.

THE MILKY WAY

The Milky Way Galaxy is a grand spiral of stars, gas and dust, stretching over 100,000 light years of space. We think of the Milky Way as the 'home' of the Sun and planets – yet the Milky Way existed long before they were born.

In this view of the Milky Way as it would have appeared only a few billion years after the Big Bang – when the Universe is only a fraction of its present age – the Galaxy has already taken on much its present form. It has a flat disc composed of stars and interstellar matter, which are in places concentrated into a spiral pattern: in this disc, new stars are continually being born. Above and below the disc are the fossil regions of our Galaxy, a halo consisting only of dead and dying remnants from the Galaxy's birth.

The Galaxy's halo is a roughly spherical region, containing a sprinkling of faint old stars. The halo marks the extent of the original gas cloud that came together to make up our Galaxy: the stars here were

the first to form. A hundred or so thickly packed clusters of stars in this region may be the remains of the individual dense small clouds that coalesced to make up the bulk of the Milky Way. Even as these first stars formed, the gas cloud continued to shrink under its own gravity, leaving the halo's stars and star clusters high and dry – like the high-water mark on the beach when the tide has gone out.

The halo is a mystery region of our Galaxy. Although only one-tenth of the Galaxy's stars reside here, astronomers have found that the halo has an immense gravitational pull on our neighbour galaxies. The strength of its gravity suggests that the halo contains a hundred times more matter than we can see. Some astronomers think that this invisible matter consists of a multitude of black holes; others that it is made up of a sea of subatomic particles.

In the centre of the collapsing gas cloud, the density rose so quickly that many stars formed at once. They

The Milky Way, our galactic home, is a flat disc of stars, gas and dust, its matter marshalled into spiral patterns that are readily seen from outside, but not so easy to discern from within. This material is constantly being recycled. Gas and dust turn into stars; dying stars eject gas and dust.

The exception to this cosmic recycling lies at the Galaxy's centre. The central bulge consists of old stars that have pursued slow-paced lives from

made up an oval-shaped core of first-generation stars that is similar to an elliptical galaxy. The rest of the gas was rotating too quickly to fall into the centre of the Galaxy. Centrifugal force whirled it outwards, into a flat disc of gas that surrounds the core of the Milky Way. The final proportions of the Galaxy – neglecting the halo – resemble a pair of fried eggs back-to-back: the egg white represents the disc, while the bulging egg yolks are the Galaxy's core.

In the disc, the matter was too thinly spread to condense into stars all at once. As a result, star birth has been going on here, at a slow rate, ever since the birth of the Galaxy. This has set the stage for a long-lived drama in the Galaxy's disc. At any one time there are stars being born, stars living more-or-less eventful lives and stars dying. Dying stars return gases to the disc, so topping up the supplies available for making new stars. This has created a cycle of star birth and star death in the disc that could continue for hundreds

of billions of years.

Most of the action in the Galaxy's disc takes place in the gaudy spiral arms, which are regions where the stars, gas and dust are especially concentrated. Photographs in fact make the spiral arms look more prominent than they should be: the arm contains only a few per cent more matter than any other part of the disc. The arms draw attention to themselves by spawning bright new stars.

As stars and interstellar matter orbit the Galaxy, they continually pass into the spiral arms and out again. They slow down as they pass through, so that there is more matter in the spiral arms than between the arms: the spiral arm is rather like a traffic jam that lives on well after the cause of the hold-up has been removed. The pile-up of matter in the spiral arms provokes the birth of stars, including some unusually brilliant stars that festoon the spiral arms with blue-white star clusters and glowing red clouds of gas.

the Galaxy's birth. And surrounding both the bulge and the disc are the faint stars of the Milky Way's halo, the first-born stars in the Galaxy.

In its overall appearance, the Milky Way has changed little in billions of years. In this reconstruction of the Galaxy in the past, any one of the faint stars in the foreground could just as easily be our Sun, for generations of stars like ours have lived and died during the history of the Milky Way.

A STAR IS BORN

The first stars were born shortly after the Big Bang, at about the same time as the galaxies they inhabit. Astronomers cannot hope to study directly how those particular stars were formed. But we are fortunate to live in a galaxy where star formation has been going on ever since – and in a part of the Milky Way where we have stellar nurseries right to hand. By studying various stars that are now at different stages of conception, gestation and birth, we can learn more about the beginnings of our own Galaxy.

Stars are born from gas and dust. These materials are scattered widely between the existing stars in our Galaxy today, and the mix must have been much the same throughout the Galaxy's life. (Astronomers studying the very first stars in the Milky Way must, however, make allowance for the fact that the dust has been ejected by dying stars: at the very beginning of our Galaxy, its material, hot from the Big Bang, would have consisted only of gas.)

Every so often, something squeezes the gas and dust between the stars, to make a smaller, denser cloud. The force may come from the explosion of a dying star, or it may be caused by the collective gravity of stars concentrated in one of the Galaxy's spiral arms. The dark dust in the cloud makes it opaque, so we see it only as a dark silhouette against the background of distant stars in the Milky Way.

But deep inside the dark cloud, hidden to ordinary telescopes, things are happening: a bunch of new stars is being conceived. The gravity of the material in the cloud is squeezing its matter ever more tightly together. This forces the gas and the dust to condense into hundreds of individual dense fragments. Every fragment is destined to become a star.

Each of these fragments continues to shrink as its own gravity tightens its grip. Inside, conditions become more extreme: matter is squeezed more tightly, the temperature soars – from a few degrees above absolute zero, it rises to 100°C, 1,000°C, 10 million degrees C: high enough to ignite nuclear fusion. As in a hydrogen bomb, hydrogen atoms begin to turn to helium, giving out energy – only here, the energy is

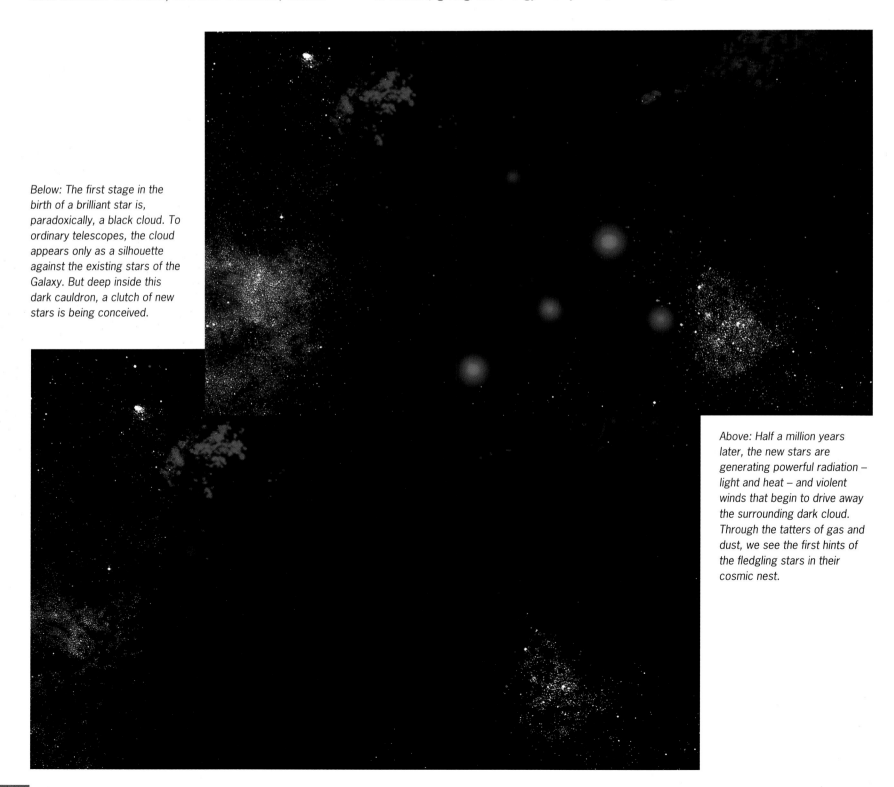

Below: The first stage in the birth of a brilliant star is, paradoxically, a black cloud. To ordinary telescopes, the cloud appears only as a silhouette against the existing stars of the Galaxy. But deep inside this dark cauldron, a clutch of new stars is being conceived.

Above: Half a million years later, the new stars are generating powerful radiation – light and heat – and violent winds that begin to drive away the surrounding dark cloud. Through the tatters of gas and dust, we see the first hints of the fledgling stars in their cosmic nest.

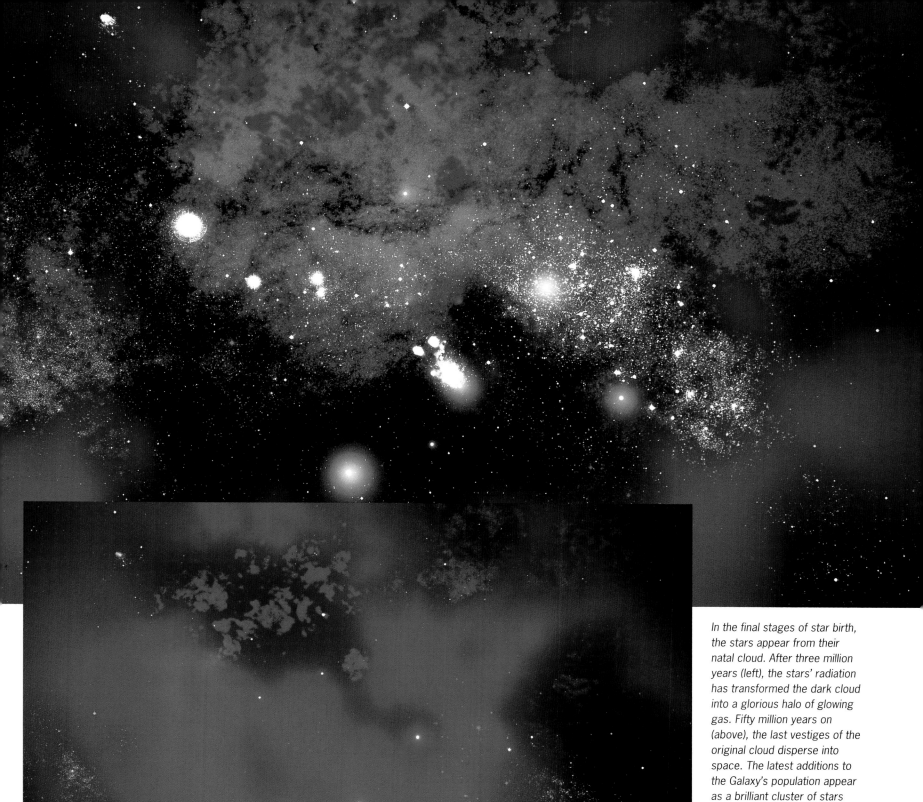

In the final stages of star birth, the stars appear from their natal cloud. After three million years (left), the stars' radiation has transformed the dark cloud into a glorious halo of glowing gas. Fifty million years on (above), the last vestiges of the original cloud disperse into space. The latest additions to the Galaxy's population appear as a brilliant cluster of stars grouped tightly together in space.

not explosive, but steadily controlled. The one-time fragment has begun to shine as a star.

However fiercely the new stars shine, they are still invisible. They are hidden deep in the dark cloud, which absorbs virtually all of the light trying to struggle through. But it is only a matter of time before the stars emerge.

The heat and light from the young stars begin to heat up the gas and dust in the cloud, making it begin to expand and thin out. High-speed streams of hot gas from the stars' incandescent surfaces rip through the cloud, tearing it to shreds. Before a million years has passed – a short time on the cosmic scale – the stars have exposed themselves to view.

Now they provide some of the most spectacular views in the Universe. The young stars light up the gas in the cloud to create glowing nebulae, where red tendrils of gas are edged with green glows or brown gauzy veils. The red coloration is the characteristic

sign of hydrogen, the most common element in the Universe, while oxygen provides the green contrast. The veils consist of dust, now being swept well away from the new clutch of stars.

Astronomers have always enjoyed turning their telescopes to these celestial showpieces. Modern techniques of colour photography show them in an even more spectacular way. The shapes of nebulae have suggested some fanciful and bizarre names – the Lagoon, the North America, the Pelican, the Rosette, the Trifid.

Eventually, the nebula's gas and dust – the afterbirth of star formation – disperse back into space. In good time, they will condense again into another dark cloud, perhaps this time to be incorporated into a star, perhaps to end up once more in a dispersing nebula of hot gases. The new stars are left alone, to live their own lives in the Galaxy's continuing cycle of star life and star death.

PROTO-STARS

Star birth is a far from gentle process. If we could see in close-up how a star forms within a dense cloud – looking in detail at the sequence depicted on the previous pages – we would observe a scene of violence in which the embryonic star can even rip apart and destroy its siblings. Astronomers call this violent star embryo a 'proto-star'.

Proto-stars are totally hidden from ordinary telescopes by the dense cloud of gas and dust that surrounds them. But telescopes that pick up infra-red radiation and radio waves can see through the dust, and witness the mayhem within – a violence that has been continuing since the Galaxy began.

The very earliest moments of star birth are, literally, obscure. Deep within a dark cloud of gas and dust there are patches of matter that are even denser and darker – just as a dingy pall of smoke contains blacker swirls. An interstellar swirl may contain as much matter as millions of Earths, and its matter has a strong enough gravitational pull to start drawing its gas and dust inwards. At this point, the formation of a new star has now become more than just a twinkle in the Galaxy's eye.

The birth of a star is a complicated and messy process. The inner parts of the swirl collapse first, to form the beginnings of the proto-star. Gas and dust from further out then fall inwards, and crash on to the proto-star. Just as a meteorite falling to the Earth becomes hot, so the infalling gases heat up to incandescence as they hit the surface of the proto-star. As more and more gas and dust fall inwards, the proto-star heats up until it is hotter than the Sun.

If we could see it stripped of its dark veils, the proto-star would now appear brilliant – brighter than it will shine when it eventually settles down to become a normal star. At this moment, its fierce heat comes purely from the energy of infalling matter, so a proto-star would cool off fairly soon after the gas and dust stopped falling on to it.

While the proto-star is still at its most brilliant, however, its centre reaches the temperature at which atoms of hydrogen begin to react together to make helium. This nuclear reaction begins to generate energy – a source of heat that will continue for billions of years. Strictly speaking, the proto-star is no more.

A star has been born.

In the short term, though, the nuclear reactor provides less heat than the energy of the infalling gases. So the precise moment of star birth is something of an anticlimax. Someone close to the proto-star would hardly notice any difference when the nuclear reactions switch on. In fact, more superficially exciting events would be distracting us from the fundamental change that is taking place in the proto-star's interior.

In a swirl of gas that is condensing, much of the matter does not fall directly towards the centre: centrifugal force provides a sideways push, so that a lot of the matter ends up in orbit around the proto-star, as a disc of gas and dust. At this stage, the whole system would look rather like the planet Saturn. There is a large gaseous proto-star shining brightly in the centre, surrounded by a thin disc of gas and dark dust.

And now the fireworks really begin. For reasons that astronomers do not yet understand, the proto-star starts to eject a powerful wind of hot gases that blows away from its surface layers. The hot gas tries to stream outwards in all directions; but around the proto-star's equator it is stopped by the dense disc of gas and dust. It can only escape in the directions in which the disc does not block its path, away from the proto-star's two poles.

Someone close to the proto-star would see two vivid streams of hot gas blowing out from its poles, like flames from a blowlamp. And, like a blowlamp, these jets of hot gas can wreak havoc. If a jet hits a neighbouring swirl of gas that is about to collapse into a proto-star, the hot gases can blast the swirl apart, aborting the embryonic star almost before it has begun to form.

The jets of gas from a proto-star blast their way through the remnants of the dark cloud that surround it, clearing away the obscuring matter so that when the proto-star settles down as a star it is visible to the outside Universe. In the meantime, the surrounding disc of gas and dust may begin to assemble into a collection of bodies that orbit the star. From the secret bedlam surrounding a proto-star emerges a stable star and its family of planets.

Right: An embryonic star, in its cosmic womb, is very active. Jets of hot gas shoot out from its poles, possibly damaging other proto-stars nearby. Dark dust swirls around its equator, beginning to condense into a system of planets. The proto-star's brilliant light, unable to escape through the surrounding dark cloud, illuminates the interior of the cavity it has excavated for itself.

1. A denser swirl within a dark cloud has enough gravity to start pulling its matter together. The collapse begins at the centre of the swirl: the matter further out will fall in later.

2. After 1,000 years, the gas at the centre has made a dense globe that is shining with the heat generated by the infall. This proto-star is surrounded by a disc of gas and dust that may form into planets.

1.

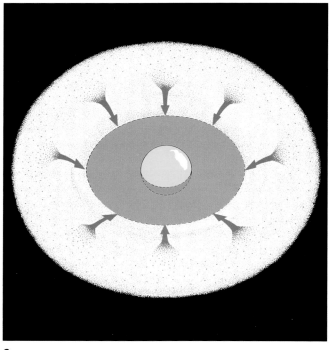

2.

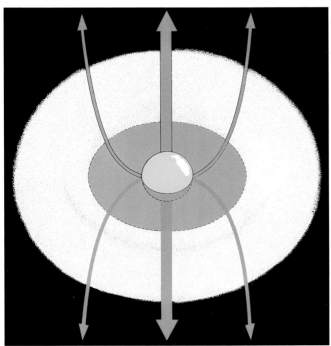

3.

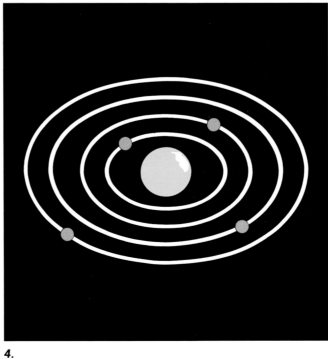

4.

3. *Ten thousand years later, the fierce energy of the proto-star drives a wind of hot gases away from its poles. At this time, the proto-star's interior experiences an even more profound change. Nuclear reactions start up, and the proto-star becomes a star.*

4. *By the time a million years have passed, the star is shining steadily. The winds from its poles have largely died down, and the material around the equator has either dissipated into space or has condensed into planets.*

STARS IN THEIR PRIME

Throughout its history, our Galaxy has contained an eclectic mix of stars. Some of the more unusual examples – such as red giants (see page 34) and white dwarfs (see page 38) – are stars that are suffering from excessive growth or shrinkage as they reach old age. But there is a wide range of character even among stars 'in their prime'.

The prime time of life for a star is a long stable period that stretches from the end of its wild excesses as a proto-star to the point when it becomes a red giant. During this period, the star remains at much the same brightness and temperature – providing a steady environment for life possibly to evolve on its planets. The Sun is at this stage, as are countless stars like the Sun back through the previous ages of the Galaxy. Many 'prime of life' stars, however, look superficially very different from the Sun.

No star in its prime can approach the sheer size of the elderly red giants, but some are twenty times larger than the Sun, while the smallest are little more than a quarter as big as our star. Some of these stars are 100,000 times brighter than the Sun; others are only 1/10,000 as luminous. While the Sun's surface is at a temperature of 5,500°C, other stars range from a dull 3,000°C to a scorching 50,000°C. We can easily tell a star's temperature from its colour. Just as a hot poker glows different colours as we heat it in a fire, so a cool star glows a dull red, while hotter stars shine yellow (like the Sun), then white hot. The hottest stars of all have a tinge of blue mixed in with the searing white.

Despite these enormous disparities, astronomers have pinned down the one crucial hidden factor that links all the stars in their prime. They all shine because they have an identical kind of nuclear reactor at their centres to produce energy – a nuclear reactor that turns hydrogen into helium.

With this vital clue, we can see these stars as a family group. The only basic difference between them is the amount of matter they started out with. The heaviest stars are the largest, the brightest and the hottest; the lightweight stars are small, dim and cool. The stars in their prime thus form a sequence, which we can arrange by mass, size, brightness or temperature. They also constitute the majority of stars in the sky, so astronomers refer to stars in their prime as 'main sequence stars'.

The heaviest stars are born with as much mass as one hundred Suns, and they are naturally rather large. The enormous pressure in the centre of these stars makes the reactions run at high intensity. The resulting immense output of energy makes the star shine intensely bright, and heats its surface to incandescence – so hot that it can shine blue-white.

A heavyweight star naturally has more reserves of 'fuel' to stoke its nuclear reactor. But the reactor is running so fast that it races through the fuel at a prodigious pace. As a result, the heaviest stars are in fact the shortest lived. A star that is a hundred times heavier than the Sun will run through its fuel supplies in only 10 million years – a blink of the eye on the celestial timescale.

A star like the Sun is moderate in everything – in size, in mass, in brightness and in temperature. With a comparatively low-key nuclear reactor at its core, such a star has enough fuel to keep it running for 10,000 million years.

The red dwarfs are lightweight stars, around one-tenth of the Sun's mass, and they are so cool that they glow only a dull red. A red dwarf consumes its nuclear fuel so slowly that it can last for hundreds of thousands of millions of years.

But even this wide range of stars probably does not exhaust Nature's ingenuity. Astronomers have argued that a lump of gas only 1/100 as massive as the Sun might condense from clouds in space. The centre of such an object would never become hot enough for nuclear reactions to begin; still, heat left over from its formation as a fiery proto-star would keep it moderately warm for billions of years.

Astronomers call such a lightweight object a 'brown dwarf'. Its mass is between that of a star and a planet. It would not shine at visible wavelengths at all, but it would emit a glow of invisible infra-red. Several astronomers have used infra-red telescopes to look for the elusive brown dwarfs – but so far without a great deal of success.

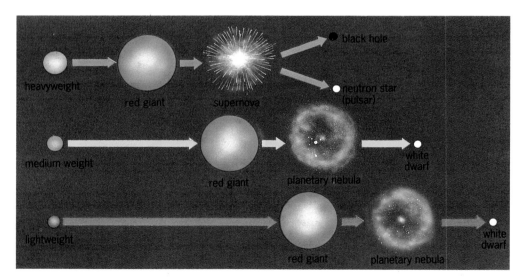

The mass of a star determines its lifetime and its ultimate fate. A heavyweight star (top) has the shortest lifespan; after expanding to a large red giant, it explodes as a supernova, leaving its core as a black hole or a neutron star. After a medium-mass star (middle), like the Sun, has become a red giant, it shrugs off its outer layers as a planetary nebula and leaves a white dwarf. A low-mass red dwarf (bottom) follows the same course as the Sun, but lives for ten times longer.

STARS IN MIDDLE AGE

As a star gets older, it experiences a severe case of 'middle-age spread'. Its diameter increases a hundredfold, so that the star becomes large enough to contain a million stars of its earlier size. At the same time, the star becomes much brighter. Its temperature also drops alarmingly: a star that previously shone at around 20,000°C may now be at only 3,000°C, and the fall in temperature brings with it a change in colour from clear white to a distinct ruddy hue. The star has become a red giant.

Because it has got so much bigger, the matter in the star is much more thinly spread. The gas in the outer parts of a red giant is much more tenuous than the air that makes up the Earth's atmosphere – although it is 'air' that is red hot, and is not transparent because it glows with its own heat. The immense bloated outer layers of the star are so far from the centre that the star's gravity has a problem holding on to them. The red giant is an unstable star, and it can wobble uncontrollably.

Many of these unstable red giants expand and contract rhythmically, with the whole star changing regularly in size. Some stars shrink to half their diameter before they increase to full size again. Scientists can describe these giant vibrations in much the same way as they describe the vibrating air in an organ pipe. An organ produces a musical note because the air in the pipe is alternately compressed and rarefied, so sending out a sound wave through the atmosphere. While the vibrations in an organ pipe repeat many times in a second, the red giant is so vast that its gas takes about a year to make one complete oscillation from its compressed to its expanded state.

As a star vibrates in and out, its luminosity changes too. Somewhat surprisingly, the star is not at its brightest when it is biggest. The complicating factor is the star's temperature, which also alters with its changing size. The star is brightest when it is hottest, and that moment occurs just after the star has reached its smallest size and is beginning to bounce back.

In contrast to the huge tenuous outer regions of the star, its very centre contains a tiny dense core. Here the matter is compressed to a density far higher than any we find on Earth. Within the hot core, nuclear reactions

An old red giant wobbles alarmingly in size. Even at its smallest, it is about a hundred times bigger than the Sun. As it gets bigger and smaller, the temperature – and the star's colour – changes. The star is hottest just after it has bounced back from its smallest size. This is the point in each cycle when the star is brightest.

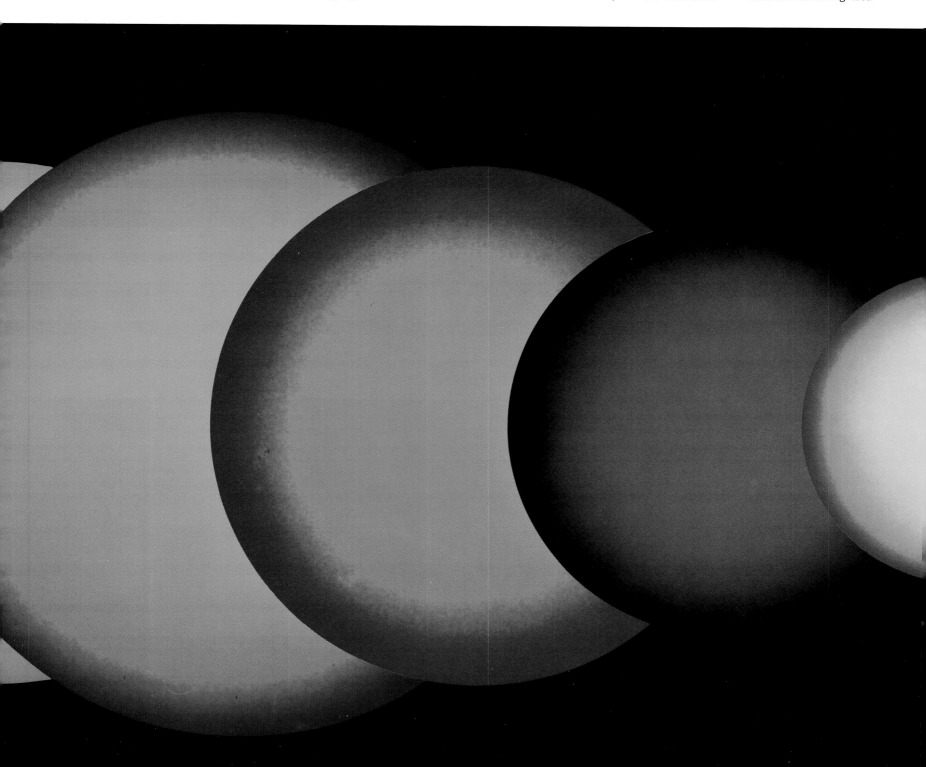

are producing the energy that makes the star shine. At an earlier stage – the 'main sequence' phase – the star's nuclear reactor converted hydrogen to helium: now the reactor is converting this helium into many heavier elements, such as carbon, oxygen and silicon.

The core of a red giant fulfils the dream of the alchemists: it converts one element into another. The first stars to form after the Big Bang consisted only of the primordial elements hydrogen and helium. During the middle years of our Galaxy's life, red giant stars were busy building up the heavier elements that we find in the Galaxy today.

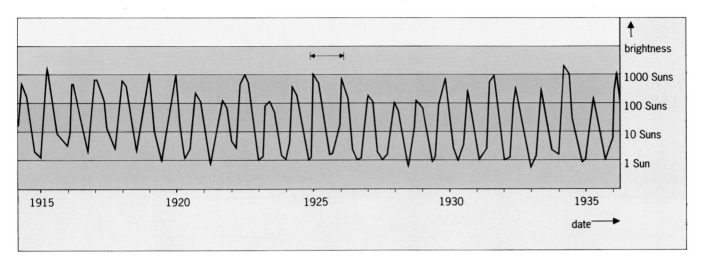

The star Mira is a good contemporary example of a pulsating red giant. Although no telescope is good enough to show its changing size, even with the naked eye we can see it regularly becoming brighter and dimmer. As shown on the graph, Mira is sometimes a thousand times brighter than the Sun, and easily visible in the sky, in the constellation Cetus. But six months later it has faded so much that a telescope is needed to see it at all. This behaviour led seventeenth-century astronomers to christen it 'Mira', 'The Wonderful'.

STAR DEATH

Every star is mortal. Even though it has a lifetime that is immense when compared to our standard three score years and ten, a star is not eternal. Sooner or later the great nuclear reactor that keeps it shining must run out of fuel. But a star does not die in vain: most stars bequeath a valuable legacy of new elements to the Galaxy that they inhabit.

A star's life expectancy depends on its mass. Heavyweight stars die young – 'young' in an astronomical context meaning 10 million years or so. A middle-weight star like the Sun can survive for 10,000 million years, while stars with the lowest masses can last for much longer still.

In the last days of a star's life, it is a red giant – an enormous ball of tenuous gas, a hundred times the size of the Sun, and pulsating in size. At its core, the star has created a pot pourri of new elements: carbon, silicon, oxygen. As its last moments tick away, the star becomes more and more unstable. Streams of gas rise and fall inside the star, dredging the new elements at its centre out to its surface. Here some of the atoms condense into soot. The dying star surrounds itself with a pall of smoke.

At the present time, we can see a good example of a smoky star in the constellation of Corona Borealis, the Northern Crown. Usually this red giant is visible to the naked eye, but every few years it puffs off a veil of smoke and disappears from sight. Telescopes that pick up infra-red radiation – which can penetrate the dust – have discovered several red giants that have totally hidden themselves in their own smoke.

Stars that died during the middle period of our Galaxy's life have polluted interstellar space. As well as soot, from stars that are rich in carbon, this pollution includes microscopic specks of rock, shed by stars that contain a great deal of silicon and oxygen. These elements are the building blocks of all the types of rock that we find on the Earth, the Moon and the other planets of the Solar System.

Eventually, the star begins to shuffle off most of its matter. The bloated outer regions of the red giant waft off into space, to form a glowing bubble of gas. These bubbles were first investigated by William Herschel in the eighteenth century. Through his small telescope, they looked very much like the planet Uranus, which Herschel had himself discovered. For this reason, he called them 'planetary nebulae' – and the name has stuck, even though in reality these bubbles have nothing to do with planets.

By cosmic standards, a planetary nebula is entirely ephemeral. Within 100,000 years, this wraith of a dead star has expanded and dissipated into the general gases between the stars.

Most stars die in the whimper of a planetary nebula, but some go with a bang – in a supernova explosion. These heavyweight stars, more massive than eight Suns, are comparatively rare in the Galaxy.

When a supernova explodes in our Galaxy, it often appears as the brightest object in our skies after the Sun and Moon – even if the exploding star is thousands of light years from us. In the year 1054, Chinese astronomers noted a luminous 'guest star' in the constellation Taurus, the Bull. We now know that it was a supernova that exploded in the outskirts of our Galaxy, some 6,500 light years away. The Chinese regarded the star as a bad astrological sign for their ruler, 'an omen that Hsin-tsung will die', as he did shortly afterwards.

A brilliant supernova seen in 1572 shook the leading astronomer of the time. Tycho Brahe, the great Dane, wrote, 'I was led into such perplexity by the unbelievability of the thing that I began to doubt the faith of my own eyes'. Both these supernovae were so brilliant that they were visible even during the day, when the bright blue sky blotted out the ordinary stars.

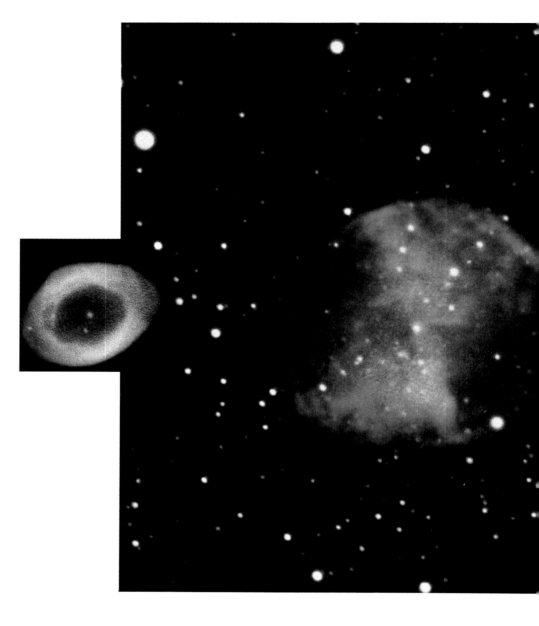

A red giant explodes because – towards the end of its life – the nuclear reactor in its centre goes out of control. Gravity squeezes the gases in its small dense core, until it collapses in on itself. The collapse liberates a burst of energy that tears the star apart, and the star literally spews its guts into space. More than the sheer brilliance and violence of the explosion, it is the ejection of matter that marks the essential role of supernovae in the history of the Galaxy, enriching our star system with a pot pourri of new elements.

The only place where nuclear reactions can create the heaviest elements – such as iron, silver and gold – is in the centre of the most massive stars. If the heavyweight stars simply died quietly, these elements would be locked away and the Galaxy at large would be devoid of elements heavier than silicon: there would be no iron, no phosphorus or sulphur – both essential to living cells – and no precious metals. It was the supernova explosions in the middle epoch of our Galaxy's history that not only created, but scattered into space, the heavy elements that now make up much of our planet and ourselves.

The Ring Nebula (above left) and the Dumbbell Nebula (above) are planetary nebulae, the bubbles of gas ejected in the death of medium-weight stars like the Sun. In the centre of each is a faint white dwarf, the exposed hot core of the old star. The Dumbbell is about one light year across, the Ring about half this size.

Both these planetary nebulae are dwarfed by the Crab Nebula (right), shown to the same scale. The Crab is a tangle of gases from a supernova explosion that marked the death of a star eight times more massive than the Sun. The faint object in the centre is a neutron star. It is the core of the original star, compressed to extremely high density in the explosion.

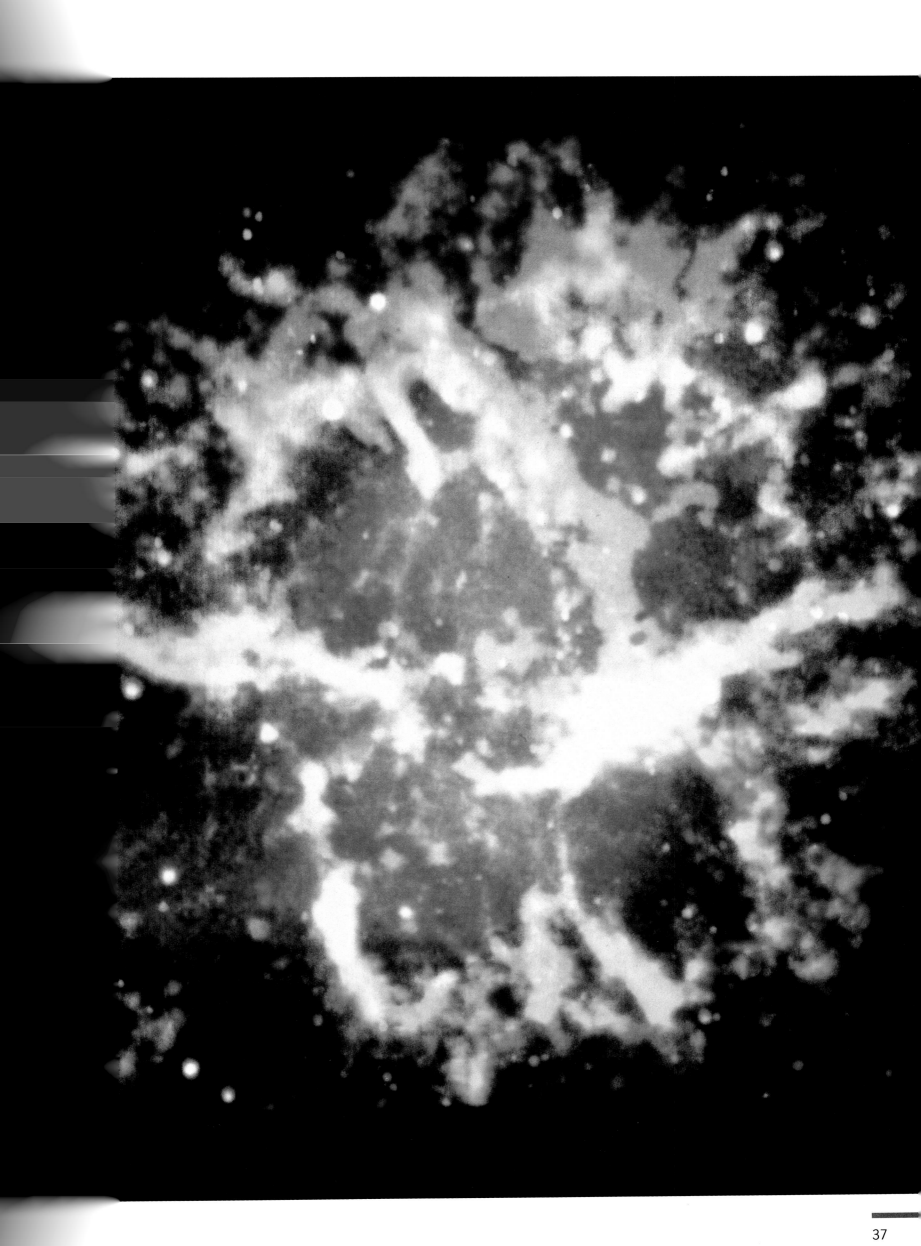

RELICS IN SPACE

Scattered among the shining stars in our Galaxy are 'dark stars' – dead relics of stars that lived and died long ago. These 'star corpses' are faint and difficult to see. But in recent decades astronomers have used sensitive techniques to identify three different kinds of dead star – white dwarfs, neutron stars and black holes.

The ultimate fate of a star depends on its mass. A relatively moderate-weight star, like the Sun, ends up as a white dwarf. This is the dense core of the original star, left exposed to space after the dying star has shrugged off its outer layers of gas. Gravity has squeezed the matter in the core tightly, compressing it to a sphere only the size of the Earth, even though it contains two-thirds as much matter as the Sun. As a result, its density is far higher than anything found on the Earth: a sugar cube of material from a white dwarf would weigh a tonne.

Because it comprises the ashes of the original star's nuclear furnace, a star core newly exposed to the Universe has an extremely high temperature, and it shines white hot. But a white dwarf does not stay white for ever. The star corpse cools down as billions of years pass by, and from yellow-hot it turns to orange and then a dim red, before eventually becoming cold and black.

The matter in a white dwarf compresses like very soft rubber. A more massive white dwarf is therefore smaller than a low-mass white dwarf, because the stronger gravity of the massive star compresses the yielding material to a smaller size. In the 1930s, an Indian physicist, Subrahmanyan Chandrasekhar, calculated that a white dwarf 40 per cent heavier than the Sun would have a size of zero. What this means, in practice, is that there cannot be a white dwarf that is heavier than 1.4 Suns.

At about the same time, Walter Baade and Fritz Zwicky, two European astronomers working in the United States, suggested that the death of a massive star such as a supernova could leave the core of the erupting star in a state even more compressed than a white dwarf. The matter in the core would all be converted into small subatomic particles called neutrons, packed tightly into a sphere only 20 kilometres across.

A neutron star contains a mass the equivalent of the Sun squashed down to the size of an island like Malta: its density is so high that a pinhead of its material would weigh a million tonnes.

Astronomers did not expect to be able to see such a small star, with any kind of telescope. But many neutron stars, it transpires, have powerful magnetic fields. These can generate a beam of radio waves that flashes past the Earth as the neutron star rotates, causing a regular stream of pulses at radio wavelengths.

In 1967, radio astronomers in Cambridge accidentally picked up pulses of radiation coming from the constellation Lacerta. At first, they thought these 'pulsars' might represent signals from an alien intelligence, but they were discovered instead to have a natural origin deep in space. A pulsar is simply a spinning neutron star. Its pulse-rate tells us how rapidly the star is turning, and in most cases this is about once a second – although there is one that rotates an astonishing 642 times every second.

According to theory, the matter of a neutron star – although dense beyond our comprehension – behaves rather like the material of the Earth. The 'star' has a thin solid crust, and a largely molten interior. When it is first formed, a neutron star is even hotter than a white dwarf, but it, too, cools down until it becomes dark against the blackness of space.

The centres of the heaviest stars become the ultimate in unseen relics: black holes. The core of a really massive star weighs several times as much as the Sun. When the surrounding star 'goes supernova', the core collapses in on itself, becoming smaller than a white dwarf and then smaller than a neutron star. As it shrinks, its gravity becomes stronger. When it is only a few kilometres across, the gravity of the star core

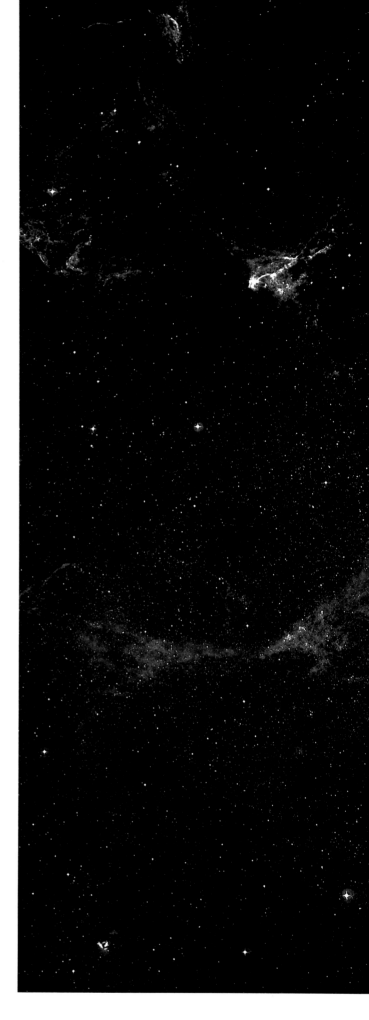

Almost invisible in the darkness of space, an old white dwarf has cooled down until it has become totally black. This dull black ball of densely compressed matter, no larger than the Earth, was once the searingly hot core of a star as big as the Sun.

Right: Star relics are all much smaller than an ordinary star, and consist of matter that is highly compressed. The three types are shown here to scale, with the Sun for comparison: all contain about the same amount of matter as the Sun, but squeezed into progressively smaller volumes.

White dwarf

Sun

Neutron star
Black hole

x1000

becomes so powerful that it can arrest even the motion of a ray of light. Light (and other radiations) can no longer escape to the outside Universe, so the star core appears completely black. The irresistible gravity also means that the core forms a 'hole' that objects can fall into, but can never emerge from.

It is impossible to see directly a black hole in the darkness of space, but astronomers do have evidence for some black holes in our Galaxy: they have caught a powerful burst of radiation from gas falling into a black hole, just before it disappears for ever from our Universe.

REBIRTH OF A STAR

For stars, death is not necessarily the end. A star corpse can sometimes revive itself by tearing matter from a companion star. So a star that disappeared from sight billions of years ago may come back to life – temporarily, at least.

A dead star can only be reborn if it has a companion. Two-thirds of the stars in our Galaxy do actually consist of a pair of stars extremely close together. (The Sun is exceptional in being a lone star.) The heavier star in the pair has a brilliant but comparatively short life, and is the first to die. Its corpse – a white dwarf, a neutron star or a black hole – generally remains in orbit around the other star.

Eventually the companion star begins to swell into a red giant. As it grows larger, its outer regions come ever closer to the star corpse. The powerful gravity of the small relic eventually rips these outer layers away from the swelling red giant, pulling the gas down in a glowing stream that whirls round in a vortex as it descends towards the dense dead star.

What happens next depends on the kind of star corpse that is feeding off its companion. The smallest kind, with the strongest gravity, is a black hole. Gas whirling faster and faster around a black hole becomes hotter and hotter. Approaching a temperature of 100 million degrees, the gas emits a torrent of X-rays before it falls inside the black hole, and abruptly disappears from view.

With a neutron star as the corpse, magnetism plays a key role. It channels the gas towards the neutron star's magnetic poles, forming two patches of superhot gas on the surface. As the neutron star rotates, beams of X-rays spin around in space like the shafts of light from a rotating lighthouse lantern.

In both these cases, the long-dead star has been resuscitated in a spectacular way: instead of shining with ordinary light, it has now become a powerhouse of X-rays. In recent years, astronomers have used

A faint white dwarf is brought back to life as it snatches gases from a companion star. The companion is swelling to become a red giant, and the concentrated gravity of the tiny white dwarf is able to pull away some of its outer gas. Because the two stars are orbiting one another, the gas falls towards the white dwarf in the form of a spiral, its temperature rising as it approaches the white dwarf in the centre of the spiral. The hot gas immediately around the 'dead' white dwarf shines more brightly than the 'living' companion star.

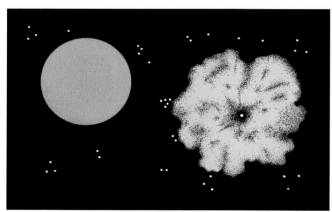

The route to rebirth. In an orbiting pair of stars, the more massive star ages more quickly and is first to become a red giant (top). It eventually sheds its outer layers as a planetary nebula (middle), exposing its core as a white dwarf. For billions of years, the white dwarf continues to orbit its companion, cooling and fading all the time (bottom). Eventually, gas from the companion will rekindle the white dwarf, as shown in the main image.

'X-ray telescopes' to detect hundreds of born-again stars, the revived corpses of stars that died during the middle period of the Galaxy's life.

Even more spectacular are the results when the star corpse is a white dwarf. The infalling gas builds up on the surface of the white dwarf, until it becomes hot and dense enough to explode as a cosmic-scale hydrogen bomb. In this explosion, the star can for a while shine as brightly as 100,000 Suns. Since the dawn of civilization, people on Earth have noted such nova eruptions in the sky, without understanding their cause. Astronomers now believe that a nova explodes several times over – at intervals of around 100,000 years – as gas regularly builds up on the white dwarf's surface and is then blown away into space.

After each eruption, some matter is left on the white dwarf, gradually building up its mass. Eventually, the star reaches the natural weight limit for white dwarfs, forty per cent more massive than the Sun. Under the force of its own gravity, the soft material of the white dwarf tries to shrink to zero size – until it reaches a point where nuclear reactions start up inside the star. Nuclei of carbon and oxygen suddenly combine together, in a reaction that rips the white dwarf apart. The ensuing explosion is the most violent kind of star eruption: not a mere nova, but a type of supernova that can shine, for a few weeks, as brilliantly as billions of Suns. These supernovae are even brighter than the explosions that mark the death of a massive star.

In the nuclear explosion, most of the white dwarf's matter turns to iron – the most stable of all the elements. In the cold of space, this iron condenses into solid grains that will eventually form part of future stars and planets. The iron atoms that make up the core of the Earth and the haemoglobin in our blood were largely forged in the explosion of white dwarf stars in the middle era of our Galaxy's life, before the Solar System was born.

HERE AND NOW

5 billion years ago to now

About 5 billion years ago, a minor event took place in one corner of the Milky Way Galaxy. Although of little significance to the Galaxy as a whole, it was an event of some importance to us: it was the birth of the Sun and its family of planets, including the Earth.

Our Solar System provides the only opportunity for us to study planets and the other small solid bodies in space. Planets are comparatively small and dark, and are difficult to spot. Our present generation of telescopes is not sensitive enough to show us even a planet like Jupiter – the giant of the Solar System – if it were orbiting the nearest star.

Astronomers in the main believe that planetary systems are the rule rather than the exception. Many very young stars have discs of solid matter circling their equators, and this matter would be expected to condense into planets in a fiery concatenation of matter. In addition, astronomers invoke the 'principle of mediocrity': the Milky Way is an ordinary galaxy, the Sun an ordinary star, so why should the Earth and the planets be anything out of the ordinary? The nine members of our planetary system are probably providing a good cross-section of the kind of planets in the Galaxy at large – objects that almost certainly outnumber the stars in the Milky Way.

So a study of the Solar System provides an in-depth survey of a typical microcosm in our Galaxy – and our observations and deductions can be checked by analyzing pieces of evidence in the laboratory. The rocky interior of meteorites, in particular, preserve many clues to the past history of the Solar System.

Investigating the planets brings us closer to understanding the greatest mystery of the Universe: the presence of life. Life, as we know it, can only exist on the surface of a planet: a star is too hot, and the matter in interstellar space is too tenuous.

The clues from our Solar System are, so far, incomplete and contradictory. We know that life can develop on a planet, because we find life on planet Earth – and fossils show that living cells developed here soon after our world itself was formed. On the other hand, Venus and Mars are similar to the Earth in many ways, and yet – as far as is known – they have never been abodes of life. Space probes have found, however, that some of the raw materials of life – organic compounds – are common in the Solar System, in bodies as diverse as a frozen moon of Saturn and Halley's Comet.

Lacking definite evidence, many astronomers argue for the existence of life elsewhere in the Universe by adopting the principle of mediocrity. Because the Solar System is, as far as we know, a typical corner of the Galaxy, there is no reason to think that our living planet is unique. As a result, there should be inhabited 'Earths' spread throughout our Galaxy – and all the other galaxies in the Universe.

BIRTH OF THE PLANETS

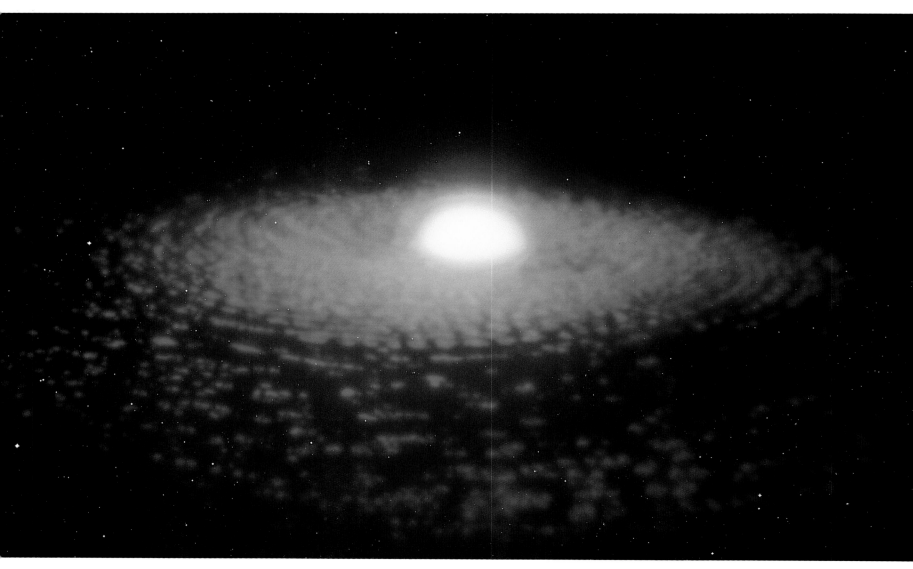

1.

The planets – including the Earth – and the Sun were born together, from a dark swirl of gas and dust in space. Its own gravity pulled this material in on itself, concentrating it into a whirling disc of gas and dust. The dense material in the centre would in time condense to become the Sun, while the rest of the disc would form into the planets, their orbital motion around the Sun still preserving the rotation of the original disc.

From fragments of ancient rock trapped in meteorites, scientists can date the birth of the Sun and planets to 4,560 million years ago. Astronomers have been able to work out the history of the early days of our planetary system, both from the evidence preserved in meteorites and from the theory of how particles of dust and larger rocks would have behaved as they whirled about the early Sun.

First, particles of interstellar dust – microscopic grains of rock and ice – jostling in the disc, began to stick together to build up fist-sized chunks of solid matter – each a loose mixture of ice and rocky dust that would have resembled a dirty snowball. At the same time, the embryonic Sun was condensing, and starting to produce intense heat. This raised the temperature of the inner regions of the disc from the sub-zero of outer space to hundreds of degrees Celsius. The ice crystals were boiled away into space, leaving only rocky pebbles orbiting the Sun in the inner part of the disc.

The pebbles in the inner Solar System and the surviving icy chunks of matter further out were now big enough to have a slight gravitational pull. Once a particle had attracted several others, the

conglomeration had a much stronger pull, attracting many more of its neighbours. So any particle that started to grow would very quickly grow into something very much bigger. This all happened in just a few thousand years. The nascent Solar System now consisted of a plethora of solid planetesimals, each a few dozen kilometres across. Near to the Sun, the planetesimals were made of rock; further out, of a mixture of rock and ice.

Planetesimals orbiting the Sun would collide. Sometimes the planetesimals were smashed into smaller fragments; sometimes the collisions were more gentle, and gravity bound them together as a single larger body. In the 1960s, the Soviet husband-and-wife team of Victor Safronov and Evgenia Ruskol worked out that, despite the destruction of planetesimals, aggregation would predominate. The end effect was to build up a few much larger worlds – the planets.

In the inner regions of the Solar System, the rocky pebbles built up worlds made of rock. In the outer regions, the ices prevailed. Here are to be found worlds of ice and planets made of water that has come from ice melted within the larger worlds.

In between are the giants of the Solar System, Jupiter and Saturn. These two worlds built up from icy planetesimals in the first instance, but their gravity became strong enough to achieve something unique: they pulled in not only solid planetesimals but also much of the gas that surrounded them. As a result, they built themselves up into gassy worlds far larger than any other planet: Jupiter, for example, could contain over a thousand planets the size of the Earth.

1. The young Sun begins to form in the middle of a swirling disc of gas and dust, 4,560 million years ago. The dust consists of microscopic pieces of rock and ice.

2. In just 10,000 years, the dust coagulates into innumerable small solid lumps that immediately accumulate into planetesimals – solid lumps up to 1,000 kilometres across. The planetesimals far from the Sun consist of ice and rock. Near to the Sun's heat, however, the original ice in the dust is boiled away, and we find lumps of rock.

3. After a million years, the billions of planetesimals have accumulated into less than a million larger bodies, the biggest about the size of the Moon.

4. Twenty million years on, a handful of the largest planetesimals have swept up most of the others, thus creating the main bulk of the nine planets that we know today.

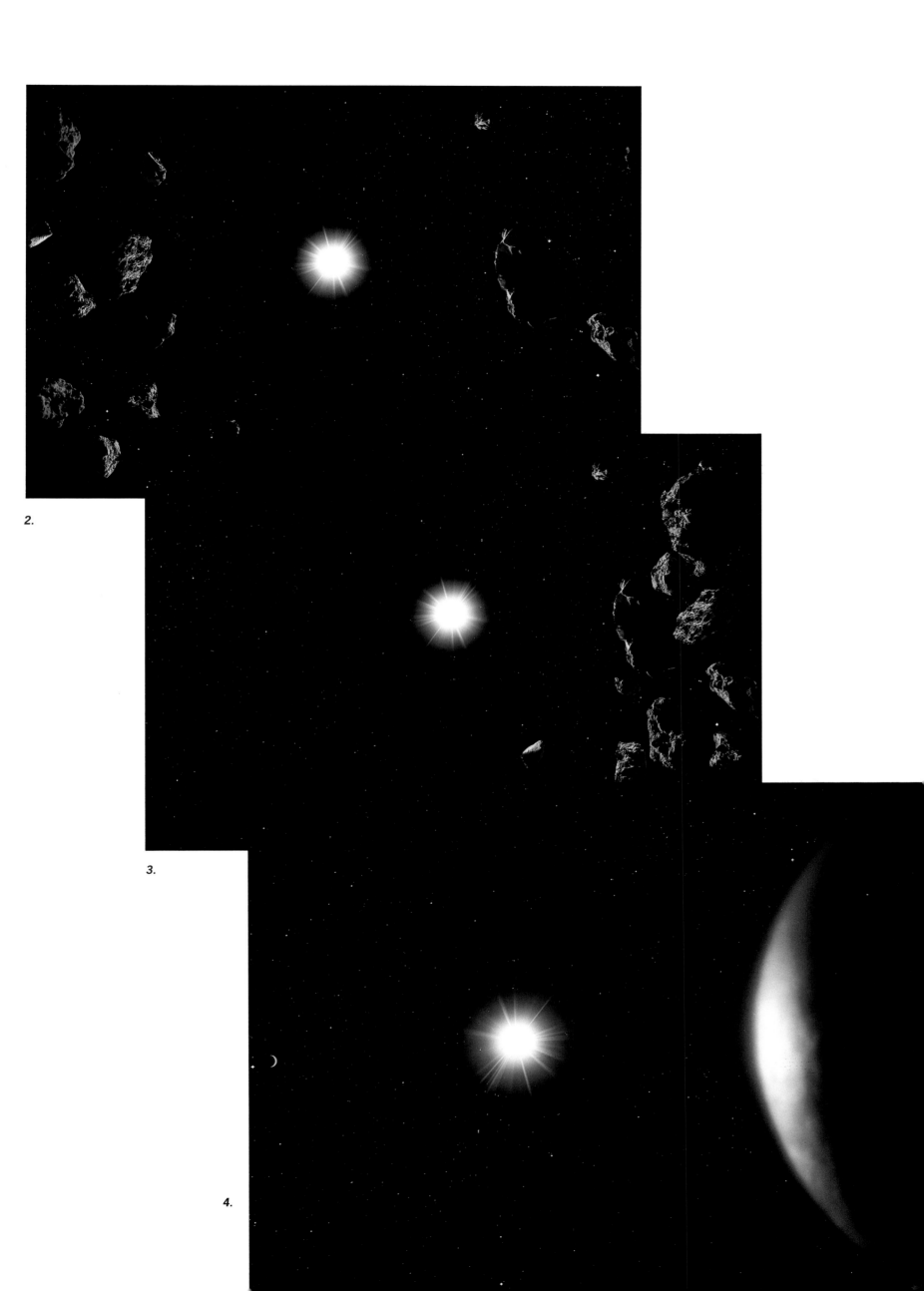

2.

3.

4.

COMETS

The appearance of a long-tailed comet, hanging in the sky like a misty sword, presaged the death of Julius Caesar, and of King Harold of England at the Battle of Hastings in 1066. But, in reality, a comet is associated with birth, not death: the birth of our Solar System.

The history of a comet begins 4,560 million years ago, when the matter around the young Sun began to assemble into planetesimals, each a solid lump several dozen kilometres across. Most of the planetesimals aggregated into the planets, from Mercury out to Pluto. Beyond Pluto, there were enough icy planetesimals to build another planet as large as Neptune, but they were too widely separated to accumulate into a single body. To this day, these million million planetesimals continue to circle the Sun, in more-or-less pristine form, in a region that stretches from the orbit of Pluto out to a distance half-way to the nearest star.

A Dutch astronomer, Jan Oort, first described this reservoir of icy planetesimals in 1950, and it is known as the 'Oort Cloud'. According to the most recent theories, most of the icy planetesimals lie in the innermost region of the Oort Cloud. As the aeons pass, some of them drift outwards. The gravity of passing stars can pull the planetesimals from their original paths, and some are sent towards the Sun.

As the icy body comes closer to the Sun, its ice starts to boil under the influence of the Sun's heat. The resulting steam breaks through cracks in the surface, to surround the small planetesimal with a huge atmosphere that can stretch a million kilometres across – larger than the Sun, though containing very little matter. The gas in the atmosphere is picked up and swept along by a stream of hot gas that is constantly flowing out from the Sun's surface, while

Jets of steam boil from the icy interior of the comet's nucleus as it approaches the Sun's heat. The surface is covered by a dark layer of rock and organic molecules, giving it a structure like a chocolate-covered ice cream.

particles of dust in the atmosphere are pushed by the sheer pressure of sunlight. These forces sweep the gas and the dust into long tails that point more or less away from the Sun. With a large gaseous 'head' and long tails, there is now a comet in our skies.

After the comet has passed the Sun, its momentum carries it back into the further reaches of space – unless the gravity of a planet affects it first. A planet can swing a comet around into a smaller orbit, so that it never returns to the Oort Cloud. Instead, it orbits the Sun in a matter of only a few years or decades. Astronomers have discovered many such 'periodic comets', but none is more famous than Halley's Comet.

The seventeenth-century scientist Edmond Halley did not actually discover this comet. But he did realize that comets seen in 1531, 1607 and 1682 were in fact successive appearances of the same comet, and

predicted that it would return in 1758. The comet did indeed turn up on time, although Halley was dead by then, and it has reappeared on schedule once every 76 years.

On its last appearance, in 1986, Halley's Comet was confronted with an international armada of spacecraft sent to see exactly what was inside a comet. Until that point, the idea that the comet's giant head and enormous tails sprang from a small icy nucleus was but theory – proposed back in 1950 by the American astronomer Fred Whipple. The nucleus was too small for astronomers to see directly from the Earth.

The European probe Giotto, hurtling through Halley's Comet at 250,000 kilometres per hour, sent back clear pictures of the nucleus as it passed at a distance of only 600 kilometres. Giotto's cameras showed that the surface of the nucleus was covered with dust and tarry substances that made it dark, while the frozen ices were largely hidden within: the nucleus resembled a huge chocolate-covered ice cream, some 16 kilometres long. The boiling ices were erupting through the dark surface in bright plumes of steam.

The space probes to Halley are just a start. Astronomers are now planning more space missions, which will culminate in the Comet Nucleus Sample Return. This spacecraft will encounter a comet, dig out some of its material, and return this scoop of cosmic ices to the Earth for scientists to analyze. We will then have in our hands a sample – preserved in deep-freeze – of the material from which the Sun and the planets were made.

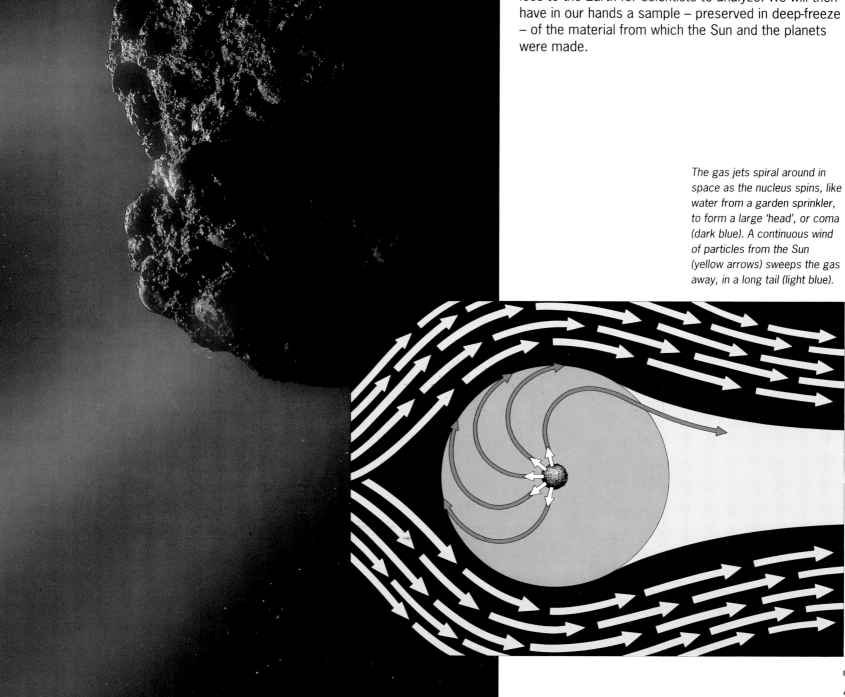

The gas jets spiral around in space as the nucleus spins, like water from a garden sprinkler, to form a large 'head', or coma (dark blue). A continuous wind of particles from the Sun (yellow arrows) sweeps the gas away, in a long tail (light blue).

PLUTO: THE FRONTIER PLANET

From the earliest times, people have known of the planets as far distant as Saturn – those that are easily visible to the naked eye. In 1781, the amateur astronomer William Herschel stumbled on the next planet, Uranus, while surveying the sky with a powerful telescope. Astronomers found that some force was pulling on Uranus, and suggested it was the gravity of an unknown planet further out. These calculations led to the discovery of Neptune, in 1846.

But some force seemed to be pulling on both Uranus and Neptune. Was it the gravity of another unknown planet? An American astronomer, Percival Lowell, calculated where this planet should be. In 1930, Clyde Tombaugh, a young astronomer at Lowell's observatory, found a planet – Pluto – just where Lowell had predicted, and following a path similar to the prediction.

To pull on the giant planets Uranus and Neptune, Pluto would have to be much heavier than the Earth. Yet it seemed too faint to be as massive as that. In 1978, astronomers discovered a moon – Charon – orbiting Pluto. They could use Charon's motion to measure Pluto's mass and its gravity directly, and found that Pluto is only 1/500 as massive as the Earth. Its gravitational pull on the other planets must be negligible. So it was no more than coincidence that Pluto matched Lowell's predictions so accurately.

Low in mass, Pluto is also by far the smallest of the planets. It would take ten Plutos to make a body the size of the next smallest planet, Mercury. The planet is only two-thirds of the diameter of the Earth's Moon.

The orbit of Pluto is tipped up, relative to the orbits of the other planets, at an angle of 17°. And it is distinctly oval, rather than circular. As a result, Pluto

Pluto and its companion, Charon, form a double planet in the outermost regions of the Solar System, far from the Sun's light and heat. As well as being of a similar size, the two worlds probably share the same atmosphere.

sometimes comes within the orbit of Neptune, so that Neptune is temporarily the outermost planet. This occurs for 20 years during each 248-year orbit of Pluto, and happens during the years 1979 to 1999.

Pluto's moon, Charon, is half as large as Pluto itself. As a result, we cannot say that Charon goes around Pluto: strictly speaking, both are in orbit about a balance point that lies between them. And the two are much closer together than any other planet and moon. As a result, most astronomers regard the Pluto-Charon system as a 'double planet'.

Charon always keeps the same face turned towards Pluto, just as our Moon keeps the same face turned towards the Earth. Unlike the Earth, Pluto keeps the same face turned towards its moon. If we lived on this side of Pluto, we would always see Charon in the sky, six times larger than our Moon appears from the Earth. Someone living on the other side of Pluto would never see Charon at all.

Lying so far from the Sun's heat, the Pluto-Charon system is unimaginably cold. Most gases would freeze into ices, on a surface at −200° C. So astronomers were surprised to find that Pluto has an atmosphere. As the planet passed in front of a distant star, in 1988, the light from the star was dimmed by layers of gas even before the star disappeared behind the planet. Even more to their surprise, the astronomers found that the atmosphere reaches way out into space – probably far enough to envelop Charon. This double planet is the only place we know where two worlds share the same 'air'.

No telescope on the Earth – not even the Hubble Space Telescope above our distorting air – can show the Pluto-Charon duo as more than a couple of faint points of light. Yet astronomers have been able to work out a great deal about these worlds, by watching assiduously as Pluto and Charon have moved in front of distant stars, and in front of one another. Changing patterns of light during these 'occultations' have revealed not only the shared atmosphere and the sizes of the two worlds, but also some details on their surfaces. Pluto is reddish around the equator, with white caps of frozen methane at its poles, while Charon is a uniform grey all over.

The origin of the Pluto-Charon system is at present unknown. Most likely, they are a pair of planetesimals that started to grow to planetary size. They would have become part of Neptune, but for a chance coincidence. Most of the bodies that crossed Neptune's orbit – as Pluto does – would have hit the embryonic Neptune and become part of that planet (or could have become a moon of the larger planet: Neptune has a large moon, Triton, that is virtually Pluto's twin). But Pluto orbits the Sun at such a rate that it completes precisely two orbits for every three orbits of Neptune. This means that whenever Pluto crosses Neptune's orbit, Neptune itself is a safe distance away, so Pluto has never been captured by the larger planet.

What we know so far of the double planet on the frontier of the Solar System has revealed rather dissimilar twins, but both – we believe – typical of the material that formed the giant outer planets, from Neptune in to Jupiter. As a result, the Pluto-Charon system has become a priority target for the next generation of spacecraft to investigate at first hand.

Pluto is very much the odd-man-out in the outer part of the Solar System. It patrols the boundaries of the Solar System in an orbit that is distinctly inclined to the orbits of the other planets. Its orbit is also so far from circular that it sometimes comes closer to the Sun than Neptune, the next planet in. And Pluto is a tiny world, only one-fifth the diameter of the Earth, while the next four planets in towards the Sun – Neptune, Uranus, Saturn and Jupiter – are giant planets, several times the diameter of the Earth.

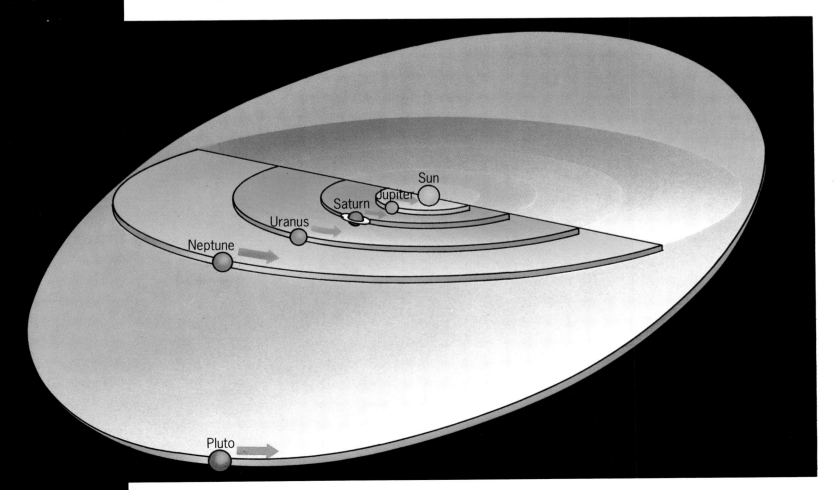

WATER AND GAS PLANETS

The four giant planets – Jupiter, Saturn, Uranus and Neptune – present a paradox in the history of the Solar System. Of all the planets, they are the most rapidly changing in appearance: Neptune's long streamers of cloud can come and go in a matter of hours, Jupiter's planet-girdling dark and light bands change from month to month, while Saturn occasionally experiences an outbreak of white spots that can wrap a band of bright clouds right round the normally dull yellow planet.

But, for all this activity, the giant worlds are also the most constant of the planets. Apart from the precise location of clouds, bands and spots, they look now very much as they did when they were first born. Even the pattern of activity that characterizes these planets has been much the same: if we looked at these worlds at any point in the history of the Solar System, we would see the same kinds of clouds, spots, bands and other meteorological activity.

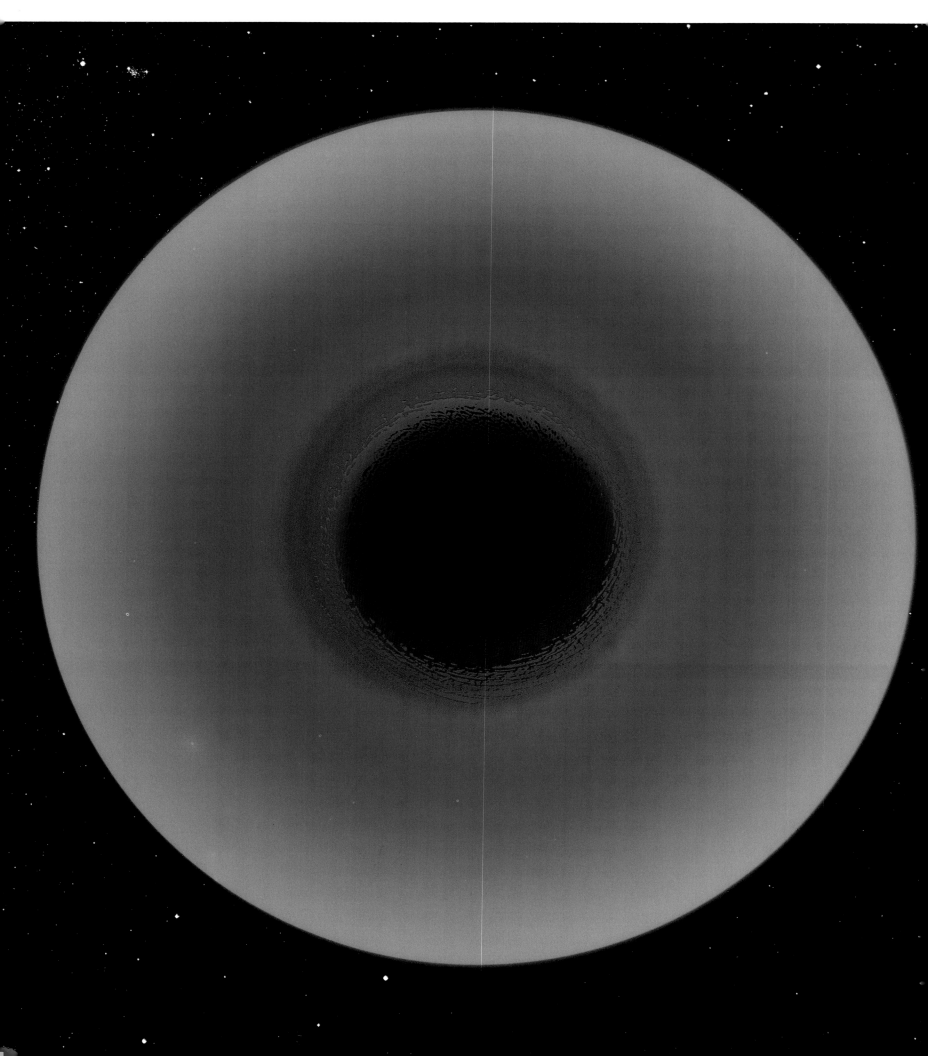

The clue to this paradox – constancy in the long term, yet continuous change in the shorter term – is that these are fluid planets. They are unlike the Earth and the other inner planets, which have solid surfaces. On the surface of a solid, rocky planet is written all that has happened in the past history of the planet. Each episode – of cratering, volcanic eruption or geological erosion – is laid down, quite literally, in tablets of stone. Later geological upheavals may destroy or cover up some of the earlier evidence, but each episode has left its trace.

The past history of a fluid planet, on the other hand, is – just as literally – written in water. The evidence of all past events, whether collisions in space or storms on the planet itself, has been wiped away as the planet's fluid continuously rearranges itself. The individual spots and clouds that we see on a fluid planet are as transitory as the eddies in a stream.

Yet there is a longer-term permanence. Just as the eddies in a stream tend to recur in the same places, so spots and cloud patterns tend to recur on a planet at certain latitudes north and south of the equator. In the case of Saturn, we know that the great white spots also recur at roughly equal intervals in time, once every 30 years or so. The white spot of 1933, discovered by comedian and amateur astronomer Will Hay, was followed by a lesser outbreak of spots in 1960, and a mammoth spot in 1990.

The outermost giant, Neptune – as befits its name – is made almost entirely of water, as is its near twin in size, Uranus. Both planets were built up from billions of icy planetesimals, resembling the nucleus of Halley's Comet or the small planet Pluto. As successive planetesimals fell into the forming planet, the impact heated them enough to melt the ice to water. Particles of dust in the planetesimals sank to the planet's centre to form a muddy core, while the planet's bulk is simply a vast ocean of warm water.

The larger giants Jupiter and Saturn started out in the same way. But they were able to capture some of the gas in the primeval disc that formed the Solar System. This gas consisted mainly of hydrogen and helium, the commonest elements in the Universe at large, and these substances now make up the bulk of Jupiter and Saturn. Although the hydrogen-helium mixture within these planets is technically a gas, it is so squeezed by gravity that it behaves like a liquid – with the same kind of rising and falling currents and swirling eddies that we find in the water planets.

Eddies just below the liquid surface of these planets produce spots and outbreaks of clouds in the thin atmosphere above. Smaller eddies can merge together to make up much larger swirling patterns. The Great Dark Spot on Neptune, for example, is as big as the Earth, while Jupiter's Great Red Spot is three times the size of our planet. Eddies deep inside the planet show their presence indirectly. They stir up the electrically conducting fluid within to generate intense magnetic fields – in the case of Jupiter, 20,000 times stronger than the Earth's magnetism.

Left: A cross-section through Uranus reveals a planet that consists almost entirely of water. It has a rocky core, with a muddy outer edge where its matter mixes with the huge ocean.

*The 'water-planets', Uranus (**1.**) and Neptune (**2.**), are very similar inside, though Neptune's atmosphere contains clouds and Uranus looks featureless. The larger giants, Jupiter (**3.**) and Saturn (**4.**), consist mainly of hydrogen and helium gases, but compressed so much that they behave rather like liquid water.*

1.

2.

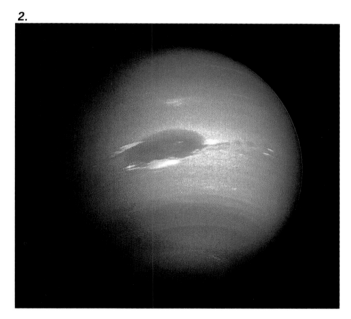

3.

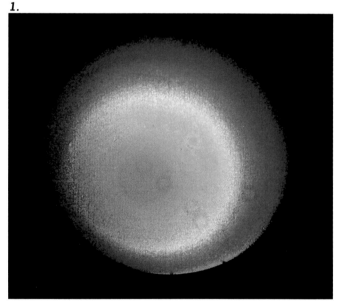

4.

RINGS

While several planets have dim ring systems, only Saturn has a brilliant encircling halo. The globe of Saturn is in fact a rather plain world, but its rings make it one of the glories of the skies, as seen through a telescope or in views from visiting spacecraft.

But Saturn was not born with the rings that we see today. A photograph of the Solar System taken a few hundred million years ago would show Saturn as a plain yellow globe, while the two outermost giants, Uranus and Neptune, would have brilliant rings. If we went back to the birth of the Solar System, we would find rings surrounding all the giant planets – and possibly some of the inner planets, including the Earth.

Astronomers now believe that a planet acquires rings when one of its moons is smashed into fragments by a cosmic collision. In the early years of the Solar System, when the planets – and their moons – formed from the accumulation of countless planetesimals, the region around a growing planet had planetesimals and embryonic moons colliding all the time as they sped around the planet.

The debris from such a collision consisted of billions of icy chunks, ranging in size from microscopic particles of dust up to the size of a house. These pieces became individual moonlets circling the parent planet, in orbits above its equator. From a distance, the individual moonlets are not visible, and the expanse of moonlets all moving in the same plane would look like a continuous sheet of matter that forms a wide bright ring around the planet.

Thus, in the tumultuous youth of the Solar System, rings were the norm, not the exception. After a planet had finished accreting, however, the bright rings began to fade. First, high-speed electrons in the planet's magnetic field hit the individual particles in the rings, tarnishing their surfaces and making them dull. More important, the ring particles were continually being broken down into smaller pieces, both by running into one another and by the abrasion of small dust particles falling in at high speed from space. Once a ring particle was itself as small as a dust grain, it felt the drag of the planet's atmosphere – and, eventually, fell into the planet's atmosphere to burn up.

By the time the Solar System was a billion years old, then, the original rings around the planets had all decayed. A planet could, however, acquire a new set of rings if one of its moons was broken up later. This may have happened several times in the history of the Solar System, but these early rings have also now long since disappeared.

But we can pick up the story a billion years ago, when the Solar System was about 3,500 million years old. Probably, none of the outer worlds had rings for a while. Then a high-speed comet crashed into one of the moons of Neptune, and another smashed into a moon going around Uranus. The debris spread into bright rings around these two worlds.

The rings gradually tarnished and thinned out, though. The particles in the rings of Uranus and Neptune became black – vying with the surface of Halley's Comet as the darkest material in the Solar

Above: Around 1,000 million years ago, Neptune had no rings. But a stray comet was on collision course with one of its moons.

Right: The collision shattered the moon and the comet into a shower of icy fragments. The myriad splinters of ice pursued their own orbits around Neptune, girdling the planet with a brilliant set of broad rings.

Below right: After 500 million years, the rings thinned and tarnished. Repeated collisions between the icy particles gradually pulverized them into a fine dust that fell down on to the planet. Electrically charged particles darkened the surfaces of the particles, making the surviving narrow rings blacker than coal.

System. As most of the matter in the rings was pulverized and fell inwards, there were a few havens at certain distances from the planet, where the gravity of a moon could assist. As a result, the remaining material was marshalled into just a few narrow dark rings. Today, the aged ring system of Uranus consists of ten of these narrow rings, while Neptune has just two thin, dark rings.

While the ring systems of Uranus and Neptune were fading from their pristine glory, however, a stray comet shattered one of Saturn's moons. This collision, only 100 million years ago, spread shiny fragments of ice around Saturn, to create the beautiful rings we see today. The glory of a ring system is transitory: as time passes, the rings of Saturn will fade just as surely as those of Uranus and Neptune have done. Our distant descendants will have to await a stray hit on some distant moon to regenerate the breathtaking sight of a fresh ring system around another planet.

MOONS

The humble moons of the giant planets provide a diary of the history of their more eminent companions. The moons have – by and large – a solid surface, on which the past is recorded, while the huge fluid planets are always erasing the evidence of their own history.

Between them, the four giant planets have most of the Solar System's complement of moons: 57 out of a total of 61 moons known at the moment. The largest moon of all, Jupiter's Ganymede, is bigger than the planets Pluto and Mercury. The two Voyager spacecraft, which passed all the giant planets between 1979 and 1989, found that these moons – made of a rock-ice mixture – are some of the most interesting and enigmatic worlds in the Solar System.

The four largest moons of Jupiter reveal that our largest planet was once almost a star in its own right. The outermost moon is a roughly equal mixture of rock and ice, but the ones closer to the planet contain progressively less ice and more rock. This sequence shows that the youthful Jupiter was once a miniature

Sun, boiling away the ice in the innermost moons and leaving more ice in the moons further out.

Later on, one of these moons, Europa, was heated inside. The ice melted and oozed upwards, to form an ocean that covered the whole moon. Exposed to the cold of space, the ocean began to freeze from the top downwards, so that Europa's surface is now covered by a totally smooth, brilliant white sheet of ice. To scale, Europa is as smooth as a billiards ball.

Its neighbour Io is even more remarkable. Caught in a gravitational tug-of-war between mighty Jupiter and its near neighbour Europa, the centre of Io has been heated to incandescence. Giant volcanoes belch sulphurous fumes over the surface of Io, and drape the landscape with long lava flows. Older volcanic deposits are covered by fresh lava and sink deeper into Io, whence they will one day erupt again. Astronomers reckon that all the material making up Io has been through a volcano at some point in its history, so that its volcanoes have effectively turned this moon inside out.

Left: An endless plain of ice makes up the smooth brilliant-white surface of Jupiter's moon Europa. It is the frozen surface of an ocean that once covered the whole of this small world.

Right: The largest volcanic eruptions in the Solar System are found on Io, another moon of Jupiter. Gases are ejected to a height of 300 kilometres, and rain down to coat the whole surface with yellow sulphurous compounds.

Right: The surface of Neptune's moon Triton is the coldest place we know in the Solar System. From its polar regions – covered by frozen methane and nitrogen – rise towering plumes of erupting nitrogen gas.

Left: Liquid ethane forms seas on the icy surface of Titan, the largest moon of Saturn. Titan is the only moon with an atmosphere denser than the Earth's, and all-enveloping clouds of organic molecules provide a constant drizzle of ethane.

Neptune's largest moon, Triton, also has volcanoes, which belch black soot from under the pink snow that makes up its polar caps. These are powered by eruptions of nitrogen gas from beneath a blanket of 'ice' that consists of nitrogen and methane. Both substances are gases on Earth, but are here frozen solid by the lowest temperatures in the Solar System.

Triton has dark secrets in its past. Long ago, it was a world circling the Sun in its own right – a second Pluto. But the young Triton passed too close to Neptune, and became a captive moon. The trauma of this event heated Triton and strange egg-carton shaped features were formed on its surface. Triton was captured in such a way that it goes around Neptune in the opposite way to the planet's own rotation – the only large moon to do so. This historical accident means that Neptune is constantly robbing its satellite of orbital energy: Triton is moving closer to Neptune, and will one day crash into the parent planet.

Saturn's moon, Titan, is a very different place. It is the only moon with a dense atmosphere – indeed, its 'air' is twice as dense as the Earth's. Suspended high in its atmosphere is a layer of orange clouds that entirely hides the surface of Titan from view. Astronomers have worked out, however, that liquid drops of ethane (an ingredient of natural gas on Earth) in the clouds should fall to the surface, and cover most of Titan with a chilly ocean of liquid ethane.

In laboratory experiments, the impact of radiation and lightning strokes can convert a mixture of gases like Titan's atmosphere to sticky orange matter rich in organic molecules – the building block of living cells. Biologists believe that such reactions produced an 'orange cloud' of organic molecules above the early Earth: these molecules were washed down into the Earth's oceans, where life proper began. Because Titan is a great deal colder, much of this organic material remains suspended in the orange clouds: like an early Earth in deep freeze. When spacecraft eventually analyze the clouds of Titan in detail, scientists expect to learn many of the mysteries of how life began on the Earth.

MERCURY: THE FOSSIL PLANET

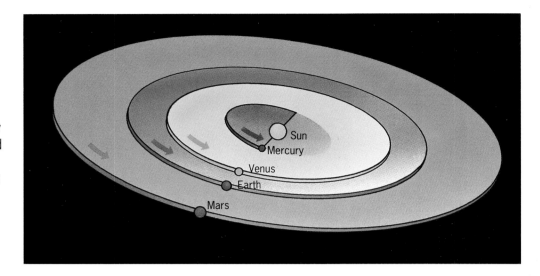

The four inner planets of the Solar System – Mercury, Venus, the Earth and Mars – have solid surfaces, whereon is engraved the story of their lives. Astronomers and geologists are working together to interpret the evidence.

The basic form of the evidence varies little from one planet to the next. A conical mountain is almost certainly a volcano, while a saucer-shaped depression surrounded by scattered rocks is probably a crater blasted out by a meteorite. The problem comes with the planets to which a great deal has happened. The later episodes tend to wipe out the evidence of what has gone before.

The largest of the rocky worlds, such as the Earth, are the best at concealing their past. A large planet contains more radioactive materials than the smaller ones, and these heat up its interior and drive volcanoes and other geological processes that renew the planet's surface. The gravity of the large planets is also strong enough to hold on to an atmosphere, which can erode the rocky evidence.

For this reason, scientists look to the small planet Mercury for a view of a planet unchanged since soon after its birth. Mercury is the smallest planet after Pluto, and is the least substantial of the four rocky worlds near the Sun. It has virtually no atmosphere to weather its rocks, and – as far as we can tell – its surface has experienced no geological upheavals or volcanic activity for billions of years.

Like the other rocky worlds, Mercury built up from a vast collection of the planetesimals that were orbiting the nascent Sun. Almost all the intermediate-sized bodies ended up inside the larger rocky planets – but one escaped this cosmic round-up and remains as the planet Mercury.

The existence of Mercury was precarious, however. According to Willy Benz and his colleagues in Cambridge, Massachusetts, another large planetesimal hit the young Mercury at high speed. Mercury narrowly avoided destruction, but the giant impact ripped off much of its outer layers. The collision may have knocked Mercury entirely from its previous orbit: according to American researcher George Wetherill, Mercury could have begun life out beyond the orbit of Mars.

This traumatic episode occurred 4,200 million years ago. From this point onwards, we can see direct

evidence on the face of the planet for the events that make up Mercury's history.

To begin with, Mercury's gravity swept up the planetesimals that remained in the inner part of the Solar System. As they hit the planet, these lumps of rock blasted out craters of all sizes, completely covering the small world with circular scars. One larger than average rock blasted out a crater with surrounding rings of mountain ranges that form a 'bulls-eye', 1,300 kilometres or so across.

Some of the rocks within the planet melted and oozed out on to the surface. The lava cooled and solidified into flat plains, which were then pockmarked by the final volleys of infalling meteorites. At the same time, Mercury shrank a little and its surface wrinkled slightly, like the skin of an old apple.

But by about 3,500 million years ago, the action was virtually over. Mercury's weak internal fires were dying out, ending its feeble geological activity, and the planet had swept up practically all the interplanetary rocks that could plummet in from space. The face of Mercury has remained virtually the same ever since.

Scientists think that all the rocky planets went through most of the stages Mercury experienced in its early history, before powerful geological forces altered their appearances. Mercury alone remains in its early state, showing us just how the other rocky planets looked early in their evolution: it is a fossil in space.

Above: Mercury is the closest planet to the Sun. It shares family characteristics with the next three planets, Venus, the Earth and Mars. All are rocky worlds, made mainly of rock and iron and having a solid surface. Mercury is the smallest, followed by Mars and Venus; the Earth is the largest of the four.

Right: The face of Mercury has been preserved from the earliest days of the Solar System. Its surface bears the scars caused by planetesimals and meteorites in the first few hundred million years of our planetary system, and a few lava plains that were extruded at that time. With no continuing geological activity and no atmosphere to erode its rocks, however, the surface of Mercury has hardly altered over the past 3,500 million years. In their early days, Venus, Mars and the Earth must have looked much as Mercury does today.

Right: Concentric curved mountain ranges form part of a 'bull's-eye' around the site of an immense impact. Here, about 4,000 million years ago, Mercury was struck by a planetesimal over a hundred kilometres across. The surface is also peppered with smaller craters from later impacts, and crossed by ridges caused by the planet shrinking slightly.

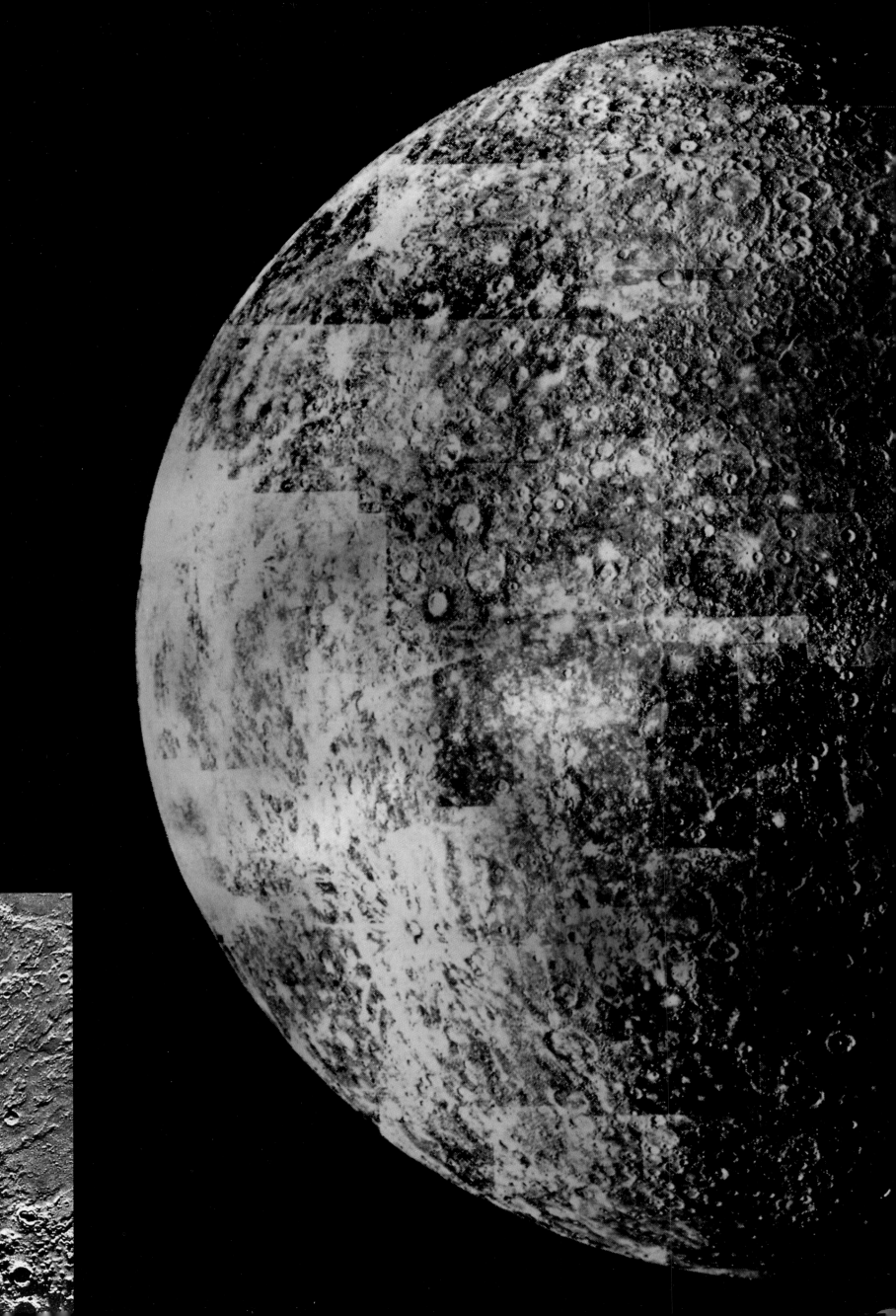

MARS: THE ICE AGE WORLD

Mars has often been regarded in science fiction as a 'second Earth' – with water and plants and intelligent Martians (usually with malevolent intentions). But spacecraft have revealed a very different world. The real Mars has air that is too thin to breathe, barren deserts, temperatures constantly below freezing – and no trace of even the lowliest form of life.

The American Mariner 9 and Viking spacecraft have provided proof, however, that Mars once did have a balmy climate. The prime piece of evidence consists of dried-up valleys in the now-barren deserts. Geologists agree that the valleys must have been carved by flowing water. This means that Mars was once warmer and that it had a thicker atmosphere, because liquid water would quickly evaporate into the thin air that Mars has today. Travelling through time, we would find that when Mars was one-tenth of its present age, the air was as dense as the Earth's and rivers flowed across its terrain, possibly into oceans that covered half of its surface.

All the evidence suggests that the first stage of Mars's life followed the lines of the fossil planet Mercury: indeed, much of Mars still has the craters that were blasted out during this period. Being a larger planet, however, Mars became hotter inside, and the planet sprang into geological action. It sprouted vast volcanoes, larger than any on the Earth even though Mars is only half the diameter of our planet. The volcanoes erupted carbon dioxide that cloaked Mars in a warming atmosphere, and water vapour that condensed and rained down on the desert.

At this time Mars looked fairly similar to the Earth. And because life began in Earth's oceans at about this epoch, many scientists believe that the waters of Mars also spawned simple living cells. But Mars was set for a big chill. The Earth has experienced ice ages many times in its history, but each time our planet has warmed up again. For Mars the ice age was to be permanent.

Scientists still debate why Mars went cold. The simplest conclusion is that the weak gravity of this small world allowed its air to leak away into space. At the same time, the planet's core was beginning to cool down, so the volcanoes began to run out of steam – quite literally – to replace the escaping gases. The protective blanket of water vapour and carbon dioxide trapped the Sun's heat, and once it had thinned Mars cooled quickly. The planet's water froze into the soil.

Other scientists believe that giant dust storms from Mars's deserts blocked out the Sun's heat for years on end, causing a drop in the planet's temperature that became irreversible. This theory, applied to the Earth, suggests that dust thrown into the air during a nuclear war would lead to a dramatic cooling of the Earth, a 'nuclear winter'. According to another theory, Mars cooled down because the last great spurt of volcanic activity raised a great bulge – the Tharsis Ridge – on one side of the planet. The unbalanced planet tipped up, changing the pattern of the seasons and so setting of an ice age.

Whatever the reason, Mars is now in the grip of an unending ice age. Its exposed deserts are barren of life. But astronomers hope that, if living cells did in fact form on Mars, some may still survive in a dormant state, perhaps buried under rocks or deep in the soil. Certainly future expeditions to Mars will look out for such organisms, and try to resuscitate them in the laboratory, by recreating the benign conditions that Mars enjoyed when it was young.

Left: About 3,000 million years ago, Mars had a climate much like the temperate regions of the Earth today. Under an atmosphere as thick as our air, streams flowed into rivers. Primitive living cells might have floated in the water. But the giant volcanoes of Mars were becoming extinct, and failing to make up the loss of the planet's atmosphere to space. On this spring afternoon, frost was beginning to form on the exposed rocks.

Below: Today, Mars's deserts are always below the freezing point of water. Because its atmosphere is less than 1/100 as thick as the Earth's, so providing little warmth, the planet's water is frozen permanently into the soil of its barren deserts. In this view from the Viking 2 spacecraft, the sky is pale with red dust, and patches of frozen carbon dioxide lie between the rocks.

VENUS: THE HELL PLANET

You are standing on a world where volcanoes are everywhere. Baleful yellow clouds drop rain of concentrated sulphuric acid. The air is made of suffocating carbon dioxide gas, and it bears down with a pressure that is 90 times the Earth's atmospheric pressure. The surroundings are hot enough to melt lead and to make the rock glow in the dark.

This could be Dante's Inferno, or the Last Judgement as painted by Bosch. In fact, you are standing on Earth's neighbour world in space, Venus.

Astronomers have long called the Venus the Earth's 'twin', because they are almost the same size. But Venus is covered entirely by clouds, and only with the advent of space probes have we been able to discover the truth about what lies beneath. From a subtle analysis of the trace gases in its atmosphere, scientists have, however, concluded that Venus might once have been a real twin to the Earth, complete with oceans, blue sky and only light wisps of cloud.

Like the other rocky worlds, the original Venus was undoubtedly covered with craters. Being a larger world

than either Mercury or Mars, Venus contained more radioactive material to melt its interior. Indeed, while Mercury never had any serious volcanism, and the volcanoes on Mars are now extinct, Venus has enough interior heat to keep its volcanoes belching at full strength to this day.

The first volcanoes to erupt from the surface of Venus supplied the planet with gases to form an atmosphere, consisting mainly of carbon dioxide and water vapour. The vapour rained down on Venus, to form seas and oceans. The liquid water dissolved much of the carbon dioxide in the atmosphere, preventing the atmosphere from getting too thick. The dissolved carbon dioxide was then 'locked away' even more safely as it reacted with the material of the ocean floor to form carbonate rocks.

Although we could not have breathed Venus's carbon dioxide 'air', in other respects the planet looked then much as the Earth does now. There were warm oceans lapping on desert shores, under blue skies laced with thin water clouds, and some scientists have suggested

Left: Venus could have passed for the Earth, 3,000 million years ago, awash with warm oceans under a clear blue sky. Simple cells may have evolved in this near-paradise.

Below: But extra heat from the Sun started to evaporate water from Venus's oceans. Water vapour is good at retaining the Sun's heat, and the temperature rapidly soared until the oceans boiled away.

that living cells might have come into existence at that time, although any traces would have been destroyed by now.

Perhaps because the Sun was becoming very slightly hotter, or because Venus's volcanoes produced too much gas, the temperature rose a little too high. Water from the oceans evaporated into the air – and water vapour is an even more efficient 'greenhouse gas' for trapping the Sun's heat than carbon dioxide. Venus's temperature increased. More water vapour evaporated.

Venus was now headed on a one-way road to Hell. Its surface became so hot that the oceans began to steam, and then to boil away. The thick pall of steam in the atmosphere helped to heat the planet even more. At the same time, there were no oceans to dissolve the carbon dioxide from the volcanoes, so this greenhouse gas also built up in the atmosphere. The temperature soared from the boiling point of water, 100°C, to 200° and 300°.

Now the heat began to decompose the carbonate rocks exposed on the old ocean floors. It began to release all the carbon dioxide that had been locked away during the planet's early life. The stage was set for the thick carbon dioxide blanket that covers Venus today, and the planet's present temperature of 470°C.

For reasons that scientists do not really understand, most of the water vapour from Venus's one-time oceans has now disappeared. Most likely, it has gradually risen above the denser carbon dioxide to the top of the atmosphere, where the Sun's radiation has broken down its molecules and sped the fragments into space.

As long as Venus had water – in clouds or oceans – it would dissolve the sulphurous gases from the multitude of volcanoes. But now the water had gone, the volcanic gases were free to rise in the atmosphere, and form their own noxious clouds. Ironically, it is this strong concoction of sulphuric and other lethal acids, now covering the entire world, that reflects sunlight brilliantly and has led to this bright planet being named after the goddess of love.

Left: With the temperature over 300°C, the rocks of the old sea floor began to decompose, releasing carbon dioxide that heated the planet even more.

Below: Venus today has a thick unbreathable atmosphere that supports clouds of sulphuric acid belched from thousands of small volcanoes. The runaway greenhouse effect has raised the temperature so much that the surface glows red-hot.

THE BIG SPLASH

The Earth is the only rocky planet with a substantial moon. Mercury and Venus have no moons, while Mars has only a pair of tiny moons that are merely small captured asteroids. Our Moon is fully a quarter of the planet's own size, so large in proportion that many astronomers refer to the Earth and the Moon as a 'double planet'.

The Moon is a relic, astronomers now believe, of a unique trauma that our planet suffered in its very early days. At that time, billions of small rocky planetesimals in orbit around the youthful Sun were coming together to make up the four rocky planets. American researcher George Wetherill calculates that the planetesimals built up the bulk of the two largest worlds, Venus and the Earth, in only 20 million years.

However, the space then surrounding Venus and the Earth was very different from today. Instead of just the two planets, Mercury and Mars, there was rocky rubble of all sizes, including several worlds the size of Mercury today and two bodies the size of Mars. These worlds were rampaging through the Solar System on oval orbits that took them across the paths of Venus and the Earth.

The American scientists Bill Hartmann and Don Davis devised the 'Big Splash' theory for the birth of the Moon, which is now accepted by most astronomers. They surmise that the 'other Mars' – a world fully half the size of the Earth – ended up on a collision course with our planet.

Travelling ten times faster than a rifle bullet, the errant world smashed into our planet. The impact cracked the crust of the Earth like an eggshell under a hammerblow. The surface near the collision point reared upwards, throwing sprays of molten rock into space. The solid ground of our planet rippled up and down in giant waves, kilometres high, that sped away from the impact site and piled up again on the far side of the Earth. The upheaval melted the rocks of the Earth's surface, leaving our planet a glowing mass of molten lava.

If our planet was convulsed, the other world suffered even more. It was completely destroyed. The force of the impact not only melted the planet right through, but boiled away the rocks at its surface. A giant plume of incandescent vapour and glowing drops of lava exploded into space.

The momentum from the doomed world carried this fountain of glowing lava fragments into orbit, to form a ring of fiery gas and liquid drops around the Earth. The ring was only a temporary adjunct to our planet, however. As if re-enacting the formation of the Solar System in miniature, the material in the ring joined together to make a world in orbit around the Earth: the Moon.

The evidence for the Big Splash is found both in the Moon's orbit and in its rocks. The Moon's orbit is very unusual. Most moons follow orbits above the equator of the parent planet – as we would expect if the moon was born along with its planet. But our Moon's orbit is considerably tilted to the Earth's equator: instead, it lies more or less in the same plane as the orbits of the planets around the Sun – as we would expect if the Moon consists of the remains of another planet.

When the Apollo astronauts landed on the Moon in 1969–72, they brought back a third of a tonne of Moon rocks. At the time, scientists thought the Moon had either once been a part of the Earth, or that it had

been a separate planet that the Earth had captured whole. The Moon rocks were sufficiently alien, however, for scientists to conclude that the Moon had never been part of our planet; nor was it a planet captured by the Earth.

Astronomers have found that meteorites have much the same mix of the different chemical elements as the Earth – which is not surprising, because our planet was built up from planetesimals that were simply larger versions of meteorites. But the Moon rocks contain very little of certain elements, such as chlorine and potassium. They are also bone-dry, with no trace of any water. What these substances have in common is that they boil at a lower temperature than the other constituents of rock. Scientists infer that the rocks making up the Moon must once have been white-hot – far hotter than the Earth or the other planets – and a Big Splash is the only obvious way of roasting the rocks so thoroughly.

After the Big Splash, the Moon formed as a world of molten rock. In the cold of space, its surface, however, soon cooled down and congealed into a solid crust. The Moon then gradually solidified from the surface to the core. Rocks fell in from space, completely covering the fresh crust with craters. The bigger impacts made large shallow basins, up to 1,000 kilometres across. With a small telescope, we can see the scars of these ancient impacts today, as a jumble of craters in the brighter regions of the Moon.

All this activity – the Big Splash and the sculpting of the lunar craters – took place between the birth of the Solar System 4,560 million years ago and some 4,000 million years in the past. By that time, the Moon had largely solidified and the rain of crater-blasting meteorites had almost ceased.

There was one final act to be played. Within the Moon's solid crust, radioactive elements heated up small pockets of rock. The resulting lava flowed out into the bottoms of the shallow basins, and solidified as huge smooth dark plains. These dry and airless plains make up the face of the Man in the Moon, and they were given fanciful names, such as the Bay of Rainbows and the Sea of Fecundity, by astronomers of previous centuries.

The Moon's lava flows solidified about 3,800 million years ago. Since then, little of consequence has happened on the Moon. Our sister world has remained a sterile museum piece in space, while the living Earth has changed and evolved.

1. About 30 million years after the beginning of the Solar System, a Mars-sized body is on collision course with the young Earth.

2. As the worlds meet, the force of the impact breaks open their crusts.

3. The oblique collision throws a plume of molten and vaporized rocks into space.

4. In a couple of hours, the hot rock has formed a temporary ring around the Earth.

5. The drops of molten rocks begin to stick together in larger lumps.

6. The lumps of rock accumulate into dozens of moonlets.

7. Only 24 hours after the impact, most of the moonlets have come together to make up the Moon.

Right: Early in the Earth's life, a body as large as Mars smashes into our world. Molten debris from the collision will condense to form the Moon.

EARTH: THE LIVING PLANET

A cosmic collision 4,000 million years ago splashed incandescent rocks into space to form a large moon, leaving the planet with a molten surface that solidified into a solid crust. Giant meteorites and comets fell from space, destroying vast tracts of land as they blasted out craters; towering volcanoes stood shoulder to shoulder in their millions as they clothed the planet in dark smoke; lightning superbolts ripped apart the clouds; poisonous vapours of sulphur and cyanide cloaked the planet.

In one of the most amazing paradoxes that we know, this satanic early Earth has matured over billions of years into the benign, beautiful and fertile planet that we inhabit today. Even more paradoxically, it was precisely the infernal early conditions that gave rise to the marvel of the Earth as it is now: living beings.

The primeval forces of infalling meteorites and superbolts of lightning – aided by the Sun's intense ultra-violet radiation – had the power to weld together the molecules of gas released by the volcanoes. These noxious emanations consisted of simple groups of two or three atoms. They were welded into larger groups, each consisting of a dozen or more atoms: molecules of sugar, molecules of organic bases, molecules of amino acids. These organic molecules may have formed into a layer of orange clouds, as we see on Saturn's largest moon, Titan.

And then the rains came. The steam from the volcanoes was condensing into water clouds, and this water eventually descended. For a million years and more, the torrential downpour continued. The waters filled the lower regions of the Earth with great oceans. The raindrops flushed down the organic molecules from the atmosphere, so that the oceans became a dilute broth of organic matter – spiced with extra molecules carried to Earth on the backs of asteroids and comets.

These molecules came together to form something greater than the sum of the ingredients. Sugars and organic bases created molecules of deoxyribonucleic acid – DNA – while amino acids assembled to make proteins. Encapsulated within small jelly-like bags, DNA and protein molecules began to work together: they made the bags grow, and then divide to produce two identical bags. The first living cells were born.

These early cells lived off the chemicals in the oceans. When these eventually began to run out, the Earth's early violence had subsided and the rains had petered out. The air was clear enough for the Sun to shine through, and cells began to use sunlight for

The crucible of life: erupting volcanoes on the early Earth created the chemicals from which living cells first formed.

energy. These were the first plants. Other individual cells became animals – surviving by the simple expedient of eating the plants, or each other.

The two types of life depended on one another. The plants breathed in carbon dioxide – then the commonest gas in the air, as it is on Venus and Mars today – and exhaled oxygen. Animal cells inhaled oxygen, and breathed out carbon dioxide. The balance of life meant that the carbon dioxide in the Earth's atmosphere dwindled, and the amount of oxygen increased until it was second only to the inert gas nitrogen. As a result of living plants, the Earth now has a unique atmosphere that is rich in oxygen.

For the first few billion years, life consisted only of single cells swimming or floating in the sea. But 600 million years ago, some cells teamed together to make larger organisms – seaweeds, jellyfish and worms. The forces of evolution drove organisms to take on more complex forms, including varieties that could colonize the hitherto barren land.

The surface – with trees and reptiles – would now be recognizably the Earth. But, although the Earth had land and sea, we would look in vain for the familiar continent shapes. Our planet's geology is as lively as its biology. Rain, ice and wind are always wearing away the land surface. More important, however, the Earth's crust is split into a dozen large 'plates', that slide around the planet. Many carry a continent on their backs, so the continents gradually drift about the surface of the globe.

Two hundred million years ago, all the continents made up a single land mass, Pangaea. Titanic forces within the Earth then split Pangaea into the continents we see today, carrying the Americas – for example – away from Europe and Africa at the same rate as a fingernail grows. About this time, the dinosaurs came to dominate the Earth. Sixty-six million years ago they perished, possibly because a giant meteorite disrupted the Earth's climate.

From the ruins of the dinosaur world emerged small hairy creatures that suckled their young. Forces of evolution once again moulded these mammals, until the Earth witnessed an animal with an extraordinary new power. *Homo sapiens* was not large or powerful, or even a model of social behaviour, but it was unique in developing abstract thought. With this power, the species has come to understand its place in both space and time: to comprehend the geography of the planet it inhabits and the wider Universe beyond, and to interpret the history of the Universe at large.

THE FUTURE

One huge region of the Universe lies for ever beyond the range of even the most complex and expensive telescope or space probe. We cannot see into this realm, and we cannot send robot craft to explore it. Yet we have one instrument – one everyday piece of equipment – that can reach out to explore this vast unexplored territory.

The unknown region is the future, the instrument is the human mind.

Human beings have a natural urge to look into the future. In everyday life, there are forecasts of everything from racing results and the weather to economic results and the results of elections. Astronomers turn their minds to predicting the future of the Universe.

There are two main reasons why astronomers have confidence in their predictions. Generations of stars around us in the Galaxy have already lived, grown old and died. By watching elderly and dying stars, astronomers have built up a good idea of what the future is for our own star, the Sun – just as we, as individuals, can anticipate that our future will follow much the same path as our parents and grandparents have already taken.

Then there is the power of calculation. Scientists have found that the Universe is made of the same kind of matter, obeying the same 'laws of nature', throughout space and time: from the innermost recesses of the atom to the farthest quasars, from the Big Bang to the present day.

Astronomers can calculate the date of a forthcoming eclipse, for example, because the Earth and the Moon follow orderly paths in space. In a similar way – though it is a much bigger task – they can predict the future of the Universe as a whole. No-one could try to foretell the fate of every individual star and galaxy, but the calculations give a broad view of what lies ahead for the Universe.

At the moment, astronomers have whittled down the ultimate fate of the Universe to two possibilities: a slow lingering death, and a sudden fiery rebirth. The uncertainty hinges on whether the Universe contains dark matter that we cannot detect with any kind of telescope but which has a gravitational pull on stars and galaxies.

In the next decade, astronomers hope to discover whether this dark matter exists. Science will then be able to answer the two key questions about the Universe that have always vexed thinkers: how did it begin, and how will it all end?

DEATH OF THE SUN

At the moment, the Sun is roughly half-way through its life. It was born almost 5 billion years ago, and over this period it has provided a steady supply of light and heat to create a comfortable abode for life on the Earth. Our planet has never frozen over totally, nor have the oceans boiled away. Mars – once a habitable world – is now in the grip of a never-ending ice age. The two planets nearer the Sun, Mercury and Venus, on the other hand, are too hot for living things of the kind that we know on Earth.

Steady as the Sun is, its heat has increased slightly since its birth. Over the next 5 billion years, the Sun will become very gradually larger and hotter, until it shines twice as brightly as it does today. The future climate of the Earth is difficult to predict precisely, especially as it will depend on the control of man-made pollutants including those that exacerbate the greenhouse effect. But the increase in the Sun's heat should melt the ice caps in the Arctic and the Antarctic, and make the polar regions the most comfortable places to live.

After this, the Sun will begin to change dramatically, marking the end of the Earth as a planet suitable for life. The Sun's central nuclear reactor – the source of all its power – will run out of hydrogen fuel. Its gravity will squeeze the material in its core tighter. At the same time, the outer parts of the Sun will grow in size.

From our perspective on the Earth, we see the Sun expanding. Its colour changes from the familiar bright yellow to a sullen orange as the temperature of the expanded surface begins to drop. Despite the slightly cooler surface, the rearrangement at the Sun's core means that it is producing more energy: we notice the Sun's heat increasing yet more. The Sun is becoming a red giant.

First to feel dire effects is Mercury, orbiting closest in. As the Sun's bloated surface engulfs Mercury, the incandescent gases melt and boil away the small rocky world. The material that once was Mercury now becomes part of the Sun's gaseous bulk. The Sun's heat boils away the heavy atmosphere of Venus, leaving its bare surface glowing red-hot in the undimmed glare of the red giant Sun.

The Earth is also barely habitable. Some of the water in the oceans evaporates as the Sun shines in the sky a hundred times brighter and hotter than today. The vapour envelops the Earth in swirling clouds that provide a temporary respite. But the Sun's heat will soon begin to boil the seas away, and the time has come for anyone living on our planet to leave – or die.

At this point, a change occurs. The inferno at the Sun's centre is now hot enough for new nuclear fires to ignite, turning helium into carbon. As a result, the Sun shrinks slightly in size – but maintains its brilliance and heat. And, in due course, the Sun will begin to grow again.

This final act will begin about 6 billion years in the future. The dying Sun is now shining a thousand times more fiercely than the Sun of today. It grows larger and larger, until its gases begin to envelop Venus. Before long, that planet too has disappeared inside the distended Sun.

Filling most of our skies, the red giant Sun will sear the now-parched deserts of the Earth, till the rocks of our planet glow red-hot. As tongues of the Sun's fire lick the surface of our planet, the rocks melt into pools of lava, and then the lava begins to boil. Earth and heaven become one red glow as the Sun engulfs our planet, and it is destroyed in the Sun's fires.

Having feasted on its first three planets, the red giant Sun is now becoming unstable. Its surface wobbles in and out, letting off – from time to time – clouds of black soot that condense from its gases. Finally, its outer layers of gas begin to stream off into space, in a riotous display of colour. They sweep past the remaining planets, to form a bubble of gas of the kind that astronomers call a 'planetary nebula'.

The Solar System now no longer has a brilliant Sun at its centre. Instead, there is a shrunken entity, a white dwarf – no larger than the present Earth – brooding over what is left of the Solar System. This is the condensed core of the Sun. It will seem, from the position where the Earth had once been, little brighter than the Moon today.

As a white dwarf, the Sun has no reserves of fuel. Like a white-hot cinder, it can only cool and fade. The remaining planets, from Mars outwards, continue in their orbits, under the gravitational mastery of this wizened star corpse, even when its light has finally gone, some 50 billion years from now. The charred remains of our Solar System – devoid of any sign of life that once existed on the Earth – are visible only as ghostly shadows in the glow of the still-shining stars of the Milky Way.

Right: Six billion years from now, the Earth is about to be engulfed by the dying Sun. The Sun has become a red giant, a hundred times its present size. It has already swallowed up Mercury and Venus, and its heat has boiled away the Earth's oceans and softened its rocks. Before long, our planet too will be but a memory.

Below:
1. The Sun is currently quite small compared to the orbits of the planets.

2. Five billion years in the future, the Sun will expand and swallow Mercury.

3. During the next billion years, the expanding Sun will devour the next planet, Venus.

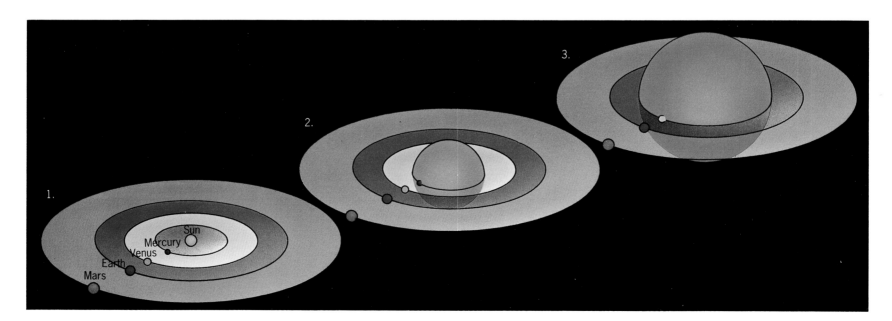

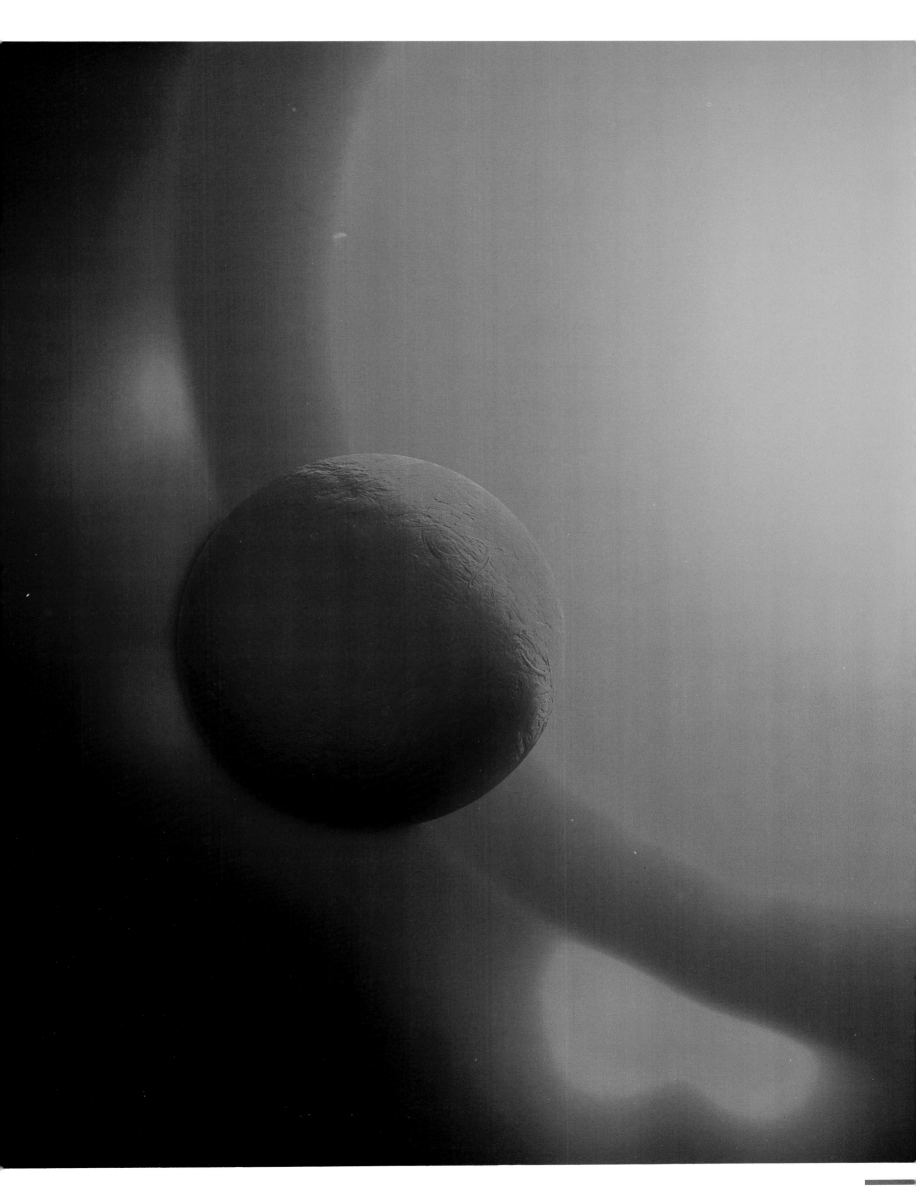

DEATH OF THE MILKY WAY

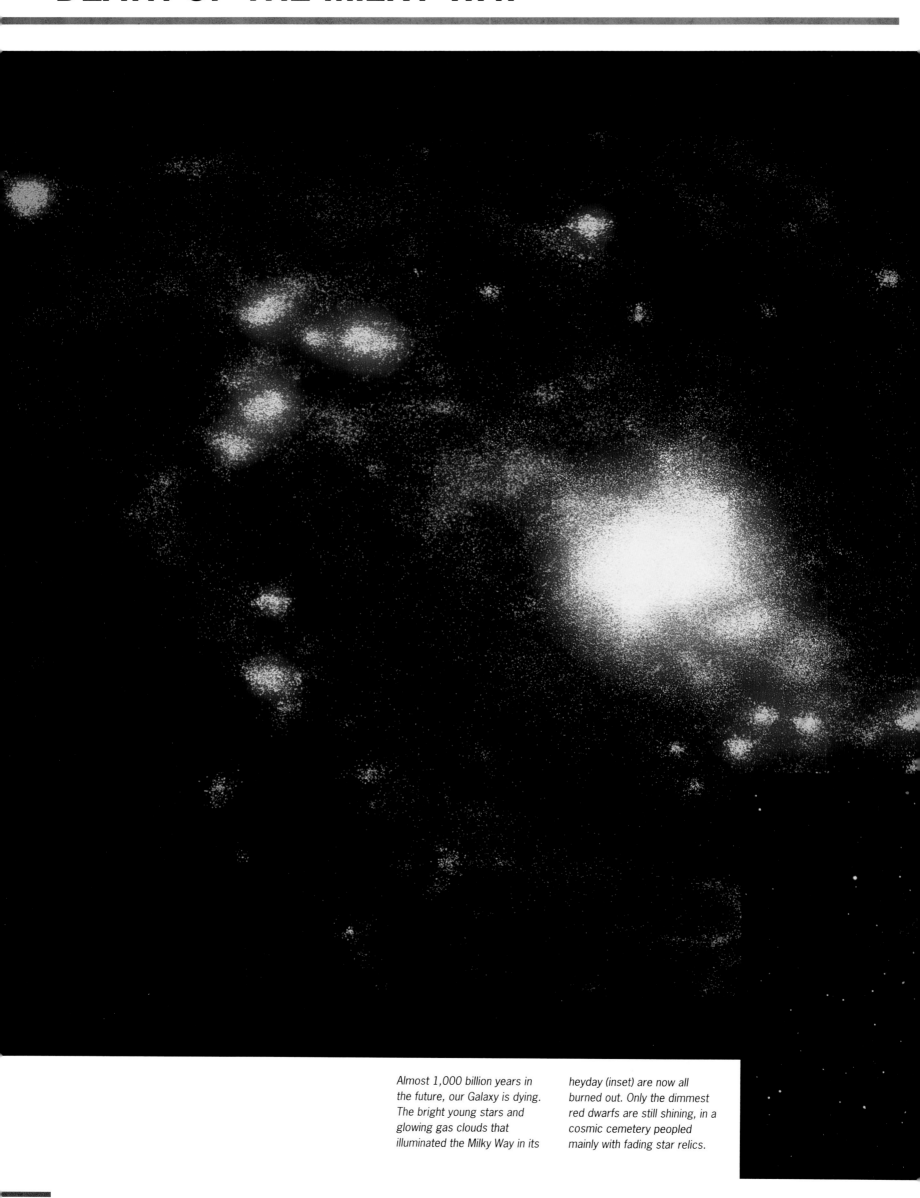

Almost 1,000 billion years in the future, our Galaxy is dying. The bright young stars and glowing gas clouds that illuminated the Milky Way in its heyday (inset) are now all burned out. Only the dimmest red dwarfs are still shining, in a cosmic cemetery peopled mainly with fading star relics.

Our Galaxy is at the present time in the prime of life. Generations of stars live and die in the spiral-shaped disc of the Milky Way. Even if a star occasionally dies in the fury of a supernova explosion, its energy is harnessed to a constructive purpose, compressing the surrounding gas clouds to such an extent that they, in turn, start to form into stars. And dying stars of all kinds leave a legacy of new elements that will enrich future stars and planets. Indeed, recycling of matter is the key to the Galaxy at the current stage of its life.

Like any recycling process, however, the Galaxy is not one hundred per cent efficient. Although a dying star returns much of its substance to space, its core is left as a tiny compact remnant – a white dwarf, a neutron star or a black hole. The matter that ends up in remnants is locked away for good, and is no use for forming further stars.

So far, this has made little difference to our Galaxy. Fully one-tenth of the matter in the disc consists of interstellar gas. This gas has mixed with the exhalation from old stars to produce new stars. Along the spiral arms, large clouds of dense gas are forming into heavy stars that are big and brilliant: brilliant blue heavyweight stars and accompanying red nebulae.

The Milky Way is now about 15 billion years old, and is currently making about ten new stars each year. Even without any recycled gas, the interstellar reservoir contains enough material to manufacture stars at the present rate for billions of years to come. With the recycled gas added in, we can safely predict that the Galaxy will look much the same for the next 100 billion years or so.

During that time, there will be changes in detail. Many astronomers believe that the Galaxy's centre harbours a dead quasar, a black hole, millions of times heavier than the Sun, that is dormant at the moment. Every so often, a cloud of gas falls towards it. The gas shines brilliantly in its final moments before it tumbles into the black hole and disappears for ever from our Universe.

The spiral pattern of our Galaxy also alters. At the moment, the Milky Way has two bright arms, with numerous small patches of stars and nebulae lying in between. The main arms may in time break up into patches themselves – and then reappear as a passing galaxy stirs them up again. At other times our Galaxy may comprise four arms, a plethora of small arms, or rings that girdle its outside.

In time, too, other galaxies may run into ours. Our two neighbour galaxies, the Large and Small Magellanic Clouds, make dangerously close encounters with the Milky Way. One day they may merge with our Galaxy, with a bright burst of star formation. Or a galaxy may pass straight through the Milky Way, splashing out the stars in our Galaxy to give it – for a while at least – the appearance of a cartwheel.

Hundreds of billions of years into the future, though, the gas between the stars is becoming thin. Dying stars still recycle their gases, but each generation is returning less than it took from the interstellar reservoir: more and more of the Galaxy's mass is now locked away in dead remnants of stars.

Some new stars are still being born, but the tenuous gas is now tending to make only small, lightweight stars – stars that are intrinsically dim. No longer are the spiral arms marked by brilliant stars and nebulae. Indeed, with only a scattering of stars being born throughout the Galaxy, it is difficult to discern any sign of the spiral arms at all.

The Galaxy is now a faint heap of embers in the blackness of space. Many of the longest-lived stars – the dim red variety – are still providing some light for the Galaxy. Here and there is the brighter spark – yellow or orange – of the occasional newly born star. The brightest of all the Galaxy's dim lights are the red giants. Each of these transitory beacons marks the last stages of one of the Galaxy's surviving stars, on the way to its doom.

From aeon to aeon, a more brilliant light flashes out occasionally to outshine the whole dull Galaxy. A star straying too close to the Galaxy's heart may be torn apart by the giant black hole lurking there, and have a moment of glory before being sucked in. In a close star pair, a white dwarf may attract so much matter from its companion that it explodes as a supernova. But these moments become rarer and rarer.

By the time 1,000 billion years has passed, the Milky Way has all but vanished. It consists of billions upon billions of black star remnants, which are virtually impossible to discern. The white dwarfs have lost their heat and have faded from sight. The neutron stars, which were once powerful beacons of radio waves, have long since made their final broadcast. And the black holes are, naturally, invisible.

For a million billion and a billion billion years, these dead stars continue to wheel around in the dead Galaxy. Beyond this, we have little conception of what will happen. Some theories suggest that all matter is ultimately unstable, and that the solid remnants will gradually fizzle out into radiation. If we wait long enough, even black holes can turn into radiation, according to the British scientist Stephen Hawking. If these ideas are correct, the cosmic graveyard that was once our Galaxy may eventually dissolve into weak radiation dispersing into the expanding Universe – if the Universe itself lasts that long.

THE END OF THE UNIVERSE

Everything in the Universe – galaxies and all their contents – are passengers riding on the back of space and time. Space and time were created in the Big Bang. Since then, time has moved onwards, and space has expanded, carrying all the galaxies (or, strictly speaking, clusters of galaxies) apart from one another at high speed.

In the simplest view of the Universe's ultimate fate, space continues to expand for ever. The galaxies are carried further and further apart. As time goes by, each individual galaxy fades out, as will our Milky Way. In the end, there will be nothing but enormous tracts of empty space, punctuated here and there by a dead galaxy. Most likely, in the far distant future, the dead matter of the galaxies will disintegrate into weak radiation, which will expand into the cold of infinite space.

Astronomers call this vision the open Universe. It is the natural way to extrapolate what we know about the expanding Universe into the indefinite future. But it neglects one important factor: gravity.

All the galaxies in the Universe are pulling on one another. This mutual attraction, across millions of light years of space, tends to restrain the expansion of the Universe. At first it might seem that the gravitational pull between the galaxies scattered over the Universe is too small to have any noticeable effect on the headlong expansion of the Universe. But, in recent years, astronomers have come to suspect that the Universe contains a quantity of matter in addition to the stars and gas that are known to make up the galaxies. The stars in the outer part of a galaxy are found to be moving so fast that, if the only gravitational constraint came from the stars we can see in the galaxy, they should fly off into space. Similarly, most clusters of galaxies should disintegrate because they do not have enough gravity to rein in their faster-moving members.

So we are led to conclude that galaxies contain a great deal of matter that is totally invisible, but that exerts a strong gravitational pull. Most theories of the Big Bang that include a period of rapid inflation also suggest there must be much matter that is unseen in the Universe today. These very different lines of argument all suggest there is at least ten times as much dark matter in the Universe as there is visible matter in the galaxies that we see.

This is in itself an astounding conclusion. What we actually see in the sky – all the stars, the planets, the clouds of gas and dust – make up only a minor part of the Universe. Most of its mass is made of something invisible, composed of some unknown substance. Beyond this, however, the dark matter has important consequences for the future of the Universe.

The dark matter in the galaxies may give them so much extra gravitational pull that they can affect the expansion of the Universe. Many scientists believe that this is a gradual effect, balanced so neatly that the expansion of the Universe will slow to a standstill only after an infinite amount of time has gone by. In practice, this is no different from the concept of the open Universe.

But it requires only a tiny proportion more dark matter for the future of the Universe to be tipped to a completely different fate – a closed Universe. If their mutual gravity is strong enough, the galaxies can slow the expanding Universe down to a standstill, in perhaps a few hundred billion years from now. Once the outward momentum has been killed, gravity takes over entirely. It starts to pull the galaxies back together again.

The expansion of space originally carried the galaxies apart from the Big Bang: now the converse happens. As the galaxies start moving together again, space begins to shrink. Faster and faster the galaxies approach, almost as if the expansion of the Universe was happening in reverse.

Time is still going forwards, however. When the Universe was at its maximum size, the galaxies were old and played out, each a necropolis of star corpses. As the Universe begins to shrink, the elderly galaxies continue to age.

In the shrinking Universe, the stage is eventually reached where the galaxies become crowded together so closely that they begin to merge with one another. If their stars were still shining, the skies would now be bright: but in fact it is dark, unilluminated by the dismal star remnants.

When the star corpses are ten times closer still, however, they begin to collide with one another. In the collisions, the hot interiors of the remnants spew out into space, in a torrent of subatomic energy. The dark is lit up by intense bursts of cataclysmic fire.

Within another twinkle of an eye, on the cosmic scale, it is all over. All the billions of galaxies, with their dead stars, have fallen together. Their matter is rekindled to incandescence in the final collapse of the entire Universe. The end of the Universe has come in the sudden finality of the Big Crunch.

As the dead galaxies fall together in the last stages of a contracting Universe, the star relics begin to collide. Sparks fly as two neutron stars smash together in a prelude to the Big Crunch.

FORWARD TO THE PAST

In the Big Crunch, the entire Universe collapses to such a small size that it can be held in the palm of the hand.

But this fiery concentration of energy cannot be kept within bounds. In an instant, it bounces back – starting to expand again. It is the seed that can generate another Universe; perhaps only one in an infinite number of Big Crunches and Big Bangs. From the Big Crunch that marks the end of our Universe we can look forward to the birth of another Universe in a new Big Bang...

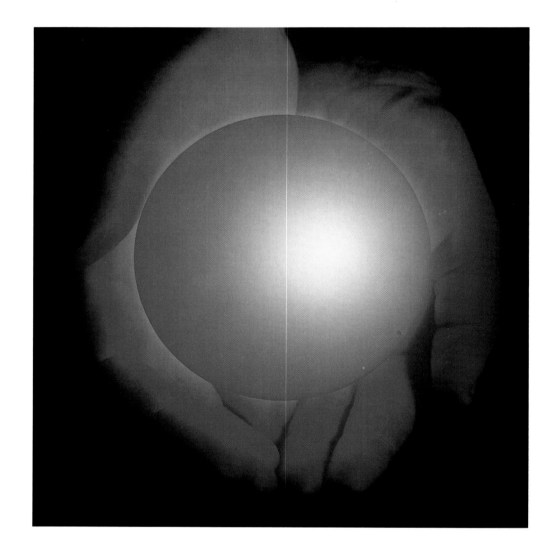

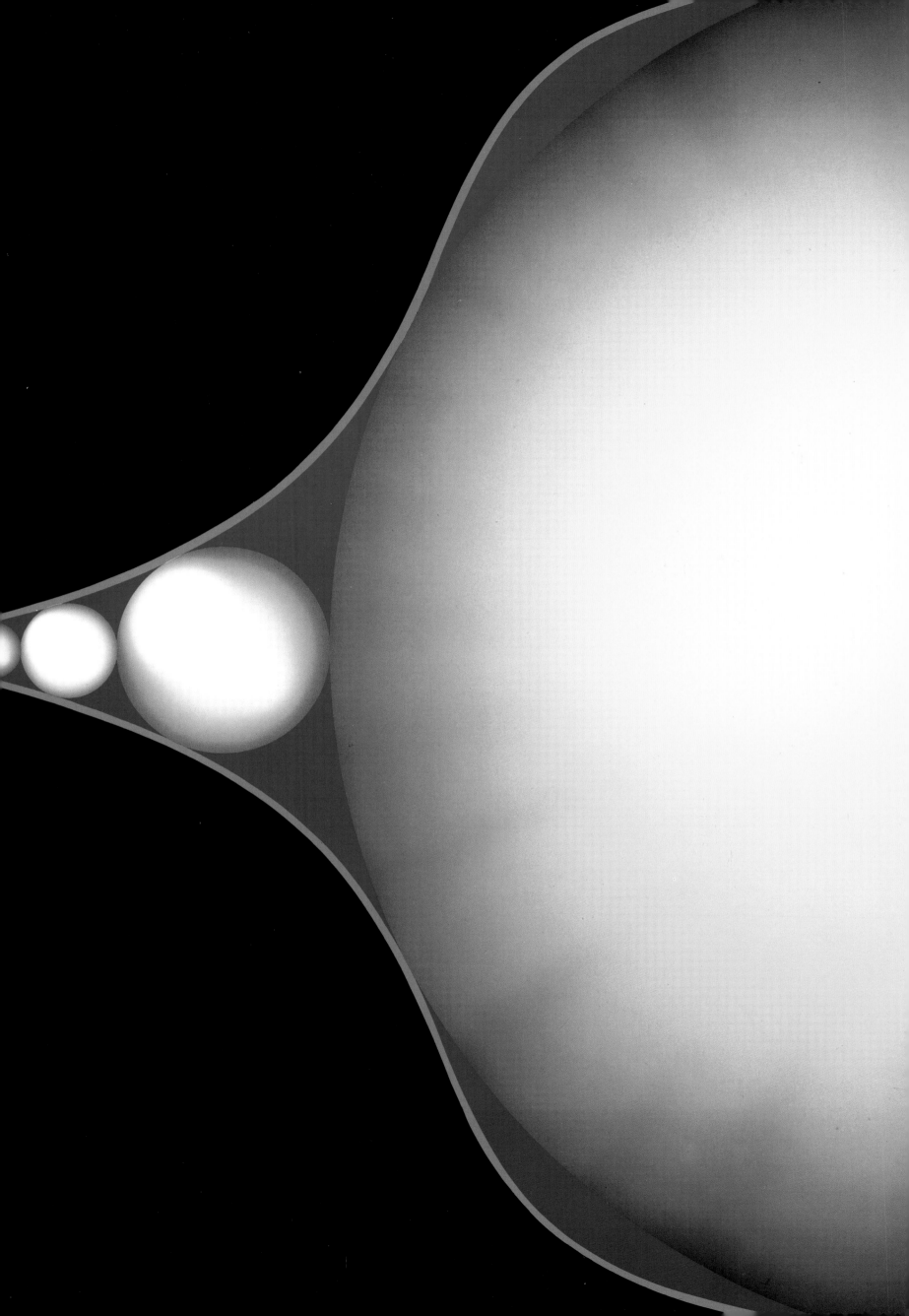

GLOSSARY

Absolute zero The lowest temperature attainable: –273°C.

Anti-matter Material that has opposite charge and other properties to ordinary matter; when anti-matter meets matter, the two annihilate in a burst of energy.

Asteroid One of several thousand rocky bodies, ranging in diameter from a few kilometres to 1,000 kilometres, that orbit the Sun. Most lie in the 'asteroid belt', between Mars and Jupiter.

Atmosphere The layer of gas surrounding a planet or moon: the air is the Earth's atmosphere.

Atom The smallest unit of an element that can exist.

Big Bang The explosion in which the Universe began, some 15,000 million years ago.

Big Crunch The postulated end of the Universe in the utter collapse of all matter.

Big Splash The most likely theory for the origin of the Moon: it invokes a large rocky body hitting the young Earth, and splashing out matter that condensed into the Moon.

Billion A thousand million (1,000,000,000).

Black hole A region of space where gravity is so strong that nothing, not even light, can escape. A black hole up to ten times heavier than the Sun can form in the centre of a supernova explosion. Black holes with over a million times the Sun's mass are found in quasars.

Brown dwarf An object intermediate in mass between a star and a planet.

Carbon dioxide A compound of carbon and oxygen, common on Venus and Mars: a cause of the greenhouse effect.

Cell (living) The smallest component of an organism that can live in its own right.

Centrifugal force An apparent outward force felt on the periphery of a rotating object.

Closed Universe A theory holding that the Universe will expand to a maximum size, and then shrink again.

Cloud (interstellar) A denser region of gas and dust in the space between the stars.

Cluster of galaxies A group of hundreds or thousands of galaxies, held together by their mutual gravitation.

Coma The large cloud of gas that forms the glowing 'head' of a comet.

Comet A small Solar System body, made of ice and rock, that can develop a large gaseous 'head' (or coma) and long tail as it approaches the Sun.

Compound (chemical) A specific type of molecule.

Constellation A pattern of stars in the sky.

Cooling flow A stream of intergalactic gas that flows into a galaxy as it cools down.

Core The central region of a galaxy, star or planet.

Crater Saucer-shaped hole in a planet or moon, blasted out by the impact of a solid body from space.

Crust A thin solid layer at the surface of a body that is molten within.

Dark matter Postulated matter that makes up much of the Universe, but cannot be detected by any kind of telescope. It reveals its existence by its gravitational pull on stars and galaxies.

Disc A flat circular arrangement of matter. Many kinds of discs are found in the Universe: stars and gas making the disc of a spiral galaxy; hot gas forming a disc around the black hole in a quasar; gas and dust making a disc around a proto-star before condensing into planets.

Double planet Two worlds of similar mass that orbit the Sun (or another star) together, for example Pluto and Charon.

Dust Microscopic solid particles of matter in the space between the stars.

Electron A subatomic particle with a negative electric charge.

Element (chemical) A particular kind of atom, for example hydrogen or oxygen.

Ethane A compound of carbon and hydrogen: gaseous on the Earth but liquid on Saturn's moon Titan.

Evolution The process of change affecting living things, astronomical objects or the Universe as a whole.

Galaxy A galaxy is a large system of stars, containing from a million to a million million stars: the Galaxy is the system in which we live, also known as the Milky Way. Elliptical galaxies are oval in shape, with little gas or dust; galaxies with gas and dust are either irregular (no particular shape) or spiral, with long curved arms.

Gravity The force that draws any two bodies together.

Greenhouse effect The increase in temperature of a planet caused by the Sun's heat being trapped by gases in the planet's atmosphere, like the glass panes in a greenhouse: the most effective 'greenhouse gases' are water vapour and carbon dioxide.

Halo A large region around a spiral galaxy populated only by very old stars.

Helium The second lightest element, and the second most common in the Universe.

Hydrogen The lightest element, and the most abundant in the Universe.

Inflation The period, a fraction of a second after the Big Bang, in which the Universe grew immensely in size.

Infra-red Radiation with a wavelength longer than light: produced by warm objects in space.

Intergalactic Space between galaxies.

Interplanetary Space between the planets.

Interstellar Space between the stars.

Light year A unit of distance, equal to 9,460,000 million kilometres (the distance light travels in one year).

Magnetism A force that affects electrically conducting substances, such as solid iron or hot gases in space.

Main sequence star A star with a core that is converting hydrogen to helium.

Mass The quantity of matter in a body. Astronomers usually compare the mass of a planet to the Earth, and the mass of stars and galaxies to the mass of the Sun.

Meteorite A solid body in the Solar System that hits the Earth or another planet.

Methane A compound of carbon and hydrogen: a gas on Earth, but frozen solid on Neptune's moon Triton and Pluto.

Milky Way The galaxy of 200,000 million stars (including the Sun) in which we live: also known as the Galaxy.

Molecule A group of atoms joined together.

Moon A moon is a small body orbiting a planet: the body orbiting the Earth is the Moon.

Nebula A cloud of glowing gas in space, lit up by hot young stars within.

Neutron A subatomic particle with no electric charge.

Neutron star A small dense body formed at the end of the life of a heavyweight star, and consisting only of subatomic particles called neutrons. A spinning neutron star is called a pulsar.

Nova An explosion of gas that has accumulated on the surface of a small white dwarf star. The white dwarf has ripped this gas from a companion star.

Nuclear fusion Nuclear reactions that involve joining together lightweight atoms to make heavier ones, for example, combining four hydrogen atoms to make one helium atom. Nuclear fusion makes the stars shine.

Nuclear reaction An interaction between the central parts (nuclei) of two atoms to produce new types of atom.

Nucleus (of a comet) The small solid ball of ice and dust in the centre of the coma **(of an atom)** the small dense region in the centre that contains most of the atom's mass.

Oort Cloud A large region around the Sun where the nuclei of comets reside before they fall towards the Sun and become visible.

Open Universe A theory holding that the Universe will expand for ever.

Orbit The path of one body around another, under the influence of gravity.

Organic molecules A compound that contains carbon atoms: living cells are made mainly of large organic molecules.

Planet A comparatively large body orbiting a star, specifically, the nine large worlds orbiting the Sun.

Planetary nebula A shell of gases ejected by a dying red giant star.

Planetesimal One of billions of solid bodies, from a few kilometres to several hundred kilometres in size, that coagulate from the dust surrounding a young star. Most planetesimals accumulate to make up planets. Some of the planetesimals and their broken fragments survive as asteroids.

Proto-galaxy A huge cloud of gas that is condensing to form a galaxy.

Proto-star A cloud of gas and dust that is collapsing to form a star; it shines because of the heat of its contraction. When nuclear reactions begin, it becomes a star.

Proton A subatomic particle with a positive electric charge.

Pulsar A rotating neutron star, emitting radiation in the form of radio waves, X-rays or light. The emission appears to pulse as the star turns.

Quark A subatomic particle that makes up neutrons and protons.

Quasar A very luminous but very small astronomical object, emitting the power of many galaxies from a region no larger than the Solar System: it is believed to be a disc of hot gas surrounding a very massive black hole.

Radio source An object in the Universe that naturally emits radio waves.

Radio galaxy A galaxy that emits radio waves.

Red dwarf A lightweight, dim and cool main sequence star.

Red giant A large star that has a low temperature: it is the final stage in a star's life, when it swells to a hundred times its previous size.

Solar System The system of objects associated with the Sun: it includes the planets and their moons and rings, asteroids and comets, as well as the Sun itself.

Star A body that shines because of nuclear reactions in its centre: the Sun is a typical star.

Starburst galaxy A galaxy where many stars are being formed at once.

Supernova An exploding star. A heavyweight star blows up at the end of its life when the nuclear reactions at its core become unstable; a white dwarf may explode if infalling gas makes it too massive.

Universe Everything that exists throughout space and time.

X-rays Highly energetic radiation that is created in regions of concentrated energy, like the hot gas found in intergalactic space or in the discs surrounding black holes or neutron stars.

White dwarf A compact star, the core of a red giant that has shed its outer layers into space.

CHRONOLOGY

After the Big Bang	Before present	
0	15 billion years	Big Bang
0.000 000 000 000 000 000 000 000 000 000 000 01 second		Inflation; temperature 1,000,000,000,000,000,000, 000,000, 000°C; mixture of matter and anti-matter
0.0001 second		Quarks annihilate anti-quarks; surviving quarks form protons and neutrons; temperature 1,000,000,000,000°C
10 seconds		Electrons annihilate anti-electrons (positrons); temperature 3,000,000,000°C
3 minutes		Some protons combine with neutrons to make nuclei of helium
300,000 years		Atoms of hydrogen and helium form as electrons begin to orbit protons and helium nuclei; this gas at a temperature of 3,000°C
500 million years	14.5 billion years	Gas filling Universe begins to fragment and form galaxies
1 billion years	14 billion years	First stars form in Milky Way
2 – 5 billion years	13 – 10 billion years	Quasars common, as gas streams into black holes in centre of galaxies; many galaxies collide
2 – 15 billion years	13 billion years – now	Cannibal galaxies grow by engulfing companions; inflows of gas make some galaxies expand
5 – 15 billion years	10 billion years – now	Milky Way in present form; continuous cycles of star birth and death
10.5 billion years	4,560 million years	Birth of Solar System; rocky dust and ice assemble into planetesimals, including nuclei of comets
	4,540 million years	Earth reaches 80% of its eventual mass
	4,530 million years	Moon born in Big Splash; another major collision strips surface rocks from Mercury
	4,500 million years	Earth and other inner planets reach their eventual sizes; large collision tips up Uranus; Neptune captures Triton
	4,440 million years	Crust of Moon solidifies (age of oldest known lunar rock)
	4,200 million years	Crusts of inner planets solidify
11 billion years	4,000 million years	Outer planets reach final size; start of lava plains on Moon
	3,960 million years	Formation of oldest rocks still surviving on Earth
	3,950 million years	Last major impacts on Moon
	3,500 million years	First life on Earth; end of major lava plain formation on Moon
12 billion years	3,000 million years	Runaway greenhouse effect on Venus; Mars loses atmosphere and freezes
	1,200 million years	First plants on Earth
14 billion years	1,000 million years	Formation of rings around Uranus and Neptune
	900 million years	First multi-celled organisms (sponges) on Earth
	800 million years	Formation of oldest surface still surviving on Venus
	600 million years	First organisms with shells on Earth
	400 million years	Life on Earth colonizes the land
14.9 billion years	100 million years	Formation of Saturn's rings; last volcanic activity on Mars
	66 million years	Extinction of dinosaurs
	3 million years	First humans
15 billion years	0	Now

After the Big Bang	After present	
20 billion years	5 billion years	Sun begins to swell, swallows Mercury then shrinks slightly
21 billion years	6 billion years	Sun swells again, engulfing Venus and Earth
	6.1 billion years	Sun sheds outer layers as planetary nebula; core becomes white dwarf
65 billion years	50 billion years	White dwarf Sun fades from sight
1,000 billion years		All stars in Milky Way become dark remnants; all galaxies dead and invisible

OPEN UNIVERSE

Infinity	Remnants evaporate into radiation, diluted to nothing in ever-expanding Universe

CLOSED UNIVERSE
Before the Big Crunch

1,000 billion years	Universe reaches maximum size; starts to contract
15 billion years	Same spacing between galaxies as now
1 billion years	Galaxies start to merge
10 million years	Neutron stars begin to collide
1 million years	Black holes swallow up remnants and gas
3 minutes	Black holes coalesce
0	Big Crunch

Photographing the Unseen

All the main images in this book have been specially created by a variety of computer and photographic techniques.

The main challenge has been to create accurate, detailed and realistic images of places that have never been photographed – and, indeed, which may not currently exist. The starting point for each image has been a detailed brief, drawn up by Nigel Henbest from the most recent astronomical ideas and discoveries. Philip Chudy has developed original techniques for realizing these scenes.

Chudy generated most of the galaxy images with a fast 80386 PC computer, using software written especially for this book by Lut Mentz. This program 'breeds' stars and distributes them randomly, but with a density governed by the actual density of stars within a galaxy. Many of these density profiles came from the Cosmos machine at the Royal Observatory in Edinburgh. The basic data for the tidal disruption of two passing galaxies (pages 20 – 21) came from a computer simulation by Françoise Combes; here the specially written software could also rotate the images to provide the most pleasing view of the encounter. After breeding the stars, the data was output to a typesetter that produced very tiny filled circles on multiple films. These were further enhanced photographically.

The computer-generated images also provided the basis for shading and other effects. In addition, digital techniques have been used to create some new images from existing photographs: for example, to replace the image of Saturn within its rings by Neptune (pages 52 – 53).

The representations of gas and solid surfaces are based on direct photography. In a few cases – such as the Big Splash (pages 62 – 63) – conventional model-making was involved, but most scenes required more original techniques. Chudy's 'clouds of gas in space' are derived from photographs of a special magnetic powder, suspended in liquid, where the magnetic attraction of the particles mimics the gravitational force in cosmic gas clouds. To avoid a sculptured and artificial look to the planetary surfaces, Chudy created them as surfaces of broken ice – suitably dyed – in a large custom-built freezer tank.

Most of the final images required multiple elements to be pieced together, using a specially designed rostrum camera that consists of a 18x24cm 10,000-joule flash projector matched to an equally large camera. In many cases, Chudy used a photograph of a real star field as background. To create the correct textural quality, each image required up to 40 different exposures and hundreds of individual flashes, with the sequence recorded on computer for consistency and control.

Acknowledgments

Our special thanks to: Royal Observatory, Edinburgh – and Quentin Parker in particular – for data and astronomical plates; Françoise Combes, Observatoire de Meudon, Paris, for data from her simulation of interacting galaxies; Lut Mentz for the computer software; L. Sandles for modelmaking and airbrush work; Niall Hendrie for photographic assistance.

Photographic credits

Nasa/Science Photo Library 2, 3, 50, 51; Earth Satellite Corporation/Science Photo Library 18, 19; Bill Iburg/Milon/Science Photo Library 37; Kim Gordon/Science Photo Library 36; Nasa/Jet Propulsion Laboratory/Science Photo Library 56; Nasa, coloured by Mehan Kulyk/Science Photo Library 57; Royal Observatory, Edinburgh 2,3; Pictor International 43; ROE/AAT Board 18, 19, 70, 71.

INDEX

Abell, George 16
Andromeda Galaxy 6, 19
Antennae galaxy 20
Apollo astronauts 62

Baade, Walter 38
Bay of Rainbows 62
Benz, Willy 56
Big Bang, The 6-13, 18-19, 74, 76, 78-9
Big Crunch 72-5, 76
Big Splash 62-3, 76
black holes 14-15, 21, 38-9, 71, 76
Brahe, Tycho 36
brown dwarfs 32-3, 76

3C 273 (radio source) 14
cannibals (supergiant elliptical galaxies) 22-3
carbon dioxide 76; on Earth 65; on Mars 58; on Venus 60-1
Centrella, Joan 11
Chandrasekhar, Subrahmanyan 38
Charon, Pluto's moon 48-9
Comet Nucleus Sample Return (spacecraft) 47
comets 46-7; coma 76; Halley's 47
Corona Borealis (Northern Crown) 36
Crab Nebula 37

dark matter, The Big Bang 10-11; stars 38-9
Davis, Don 62
Dumbbell Nebula 36
dwarf galaxies 12-13; elliptical 18

Earth,
    birth of the Moon 62-3
    birth of 44-5, 64-5
    continental plates 65
    death of the Sun 68-9
    life on 64-5
    and Mercury, Venus and Mars 56-61
elliptical galaxies 18-19; supergiant 22-3
end of the Universe 72-3
Europa, Jupiter's moon 54
expanding galaxies 16-17
expansion of space and the Universe 8-9

Fabian, Andy 16
galaxies,
    close encounters between 20-1
    different kinds 18-19
    dwarf 12-13; elliptical 18
    expanding 16-17
    formation of 6, 10-13
    Large and Small Magellanic Clouds 71
    radio galaxy 14, 77
    Solar System and 42-3
    spiral 18-19, 24-5
    starburst 21
    superclusters of 12-13
    supergiant elliptical (cannibals) 22-3
    see also Milky Way
Ganymede, Jupiter's moon 54
giant elliptical galaxy 18-19
Giotto (European spacecraft) 47
gravity 76; and the Universe 8-9, 72-3
Great Dark Spot on Neptune 51
Great Red Spot on Jupiter 51
greenhouse effect 68, 76
Guth, Alan 8

Halley's Comet, Edmond Halley 47
Hartmann, Bill 62
Hawking, Stephen 71
Hercules constellation 22

Herschel, William 36, 48
homo sapiens (human beings) 6, 65
Hubble Space Telescope 49

Io, Jupiter's moon 54

Jupiter 44, 49, 50-1, 54, 76

Lacerta constellation 38
life,
    DNA and proteins 64
    evolution and 65
    Solar System and 42
    Titan and 55
Lowell, Percival 48

Magellanic Clouds, Large and Small 71
Mariner 9 (spacecraft) 58
Mars 56, 58-9; asteroid belt 76
Melott, Adrian 11
Mercury 46, 48, 56-7; death of the Sun 68-9
Mice galaxy, The 20
Milky Way 26-7, 76
    construction of 11
    death of the 70-1
    formation of 12-13
    life of stars and the 24-5
    number of stars in 18
    Solar System and 42-3
    spiral galaxy 19
Mira 35
moons,
    Earth's 49, 62-3; landings on 62
    Jupiter's Ganymede, Europa and Io 54
    Neptune's Triton 55
    Pluto's Charon 48-9
    Saturn's Titan 55

nebulae 29, 36-7, 77
Neptune 46, 48-53; moons 55
NGC 6166 22
Northern Crown (Corona Borealis) 36
nuclear reactions 34-5, 41, 68, 77

one-armed spiral galaxy 18-19
Oort Cloud 46-7, 77; Jan Oort 46

Pangaea 65
Pegasus and Perseus 11
planetary nebulae 36, 77
planetesimals 44-6, 56, 77
planets,
    birth of 44-5
    comets and the 46-7
    Earth 44-5, 56-65, 68-9
    Jupiter 44, 49, 50-1, 54, 76
    Mars 56, 58-9, 76
    Mercury 46, 48, 56-7, 68-9
    moons 48-9, 54-5
    Neptune 46, 48-53, 55
    Pluto 46, 48-9
    rings 52-3
    Saturn 44, 49-53, 55
    Uranus 48-51
    Venus 56, 60-1
    water and gas 50-1
Pluto 46, 48-9
proto-galaxies 12-13, 77
proto-stars 30-1, 77
protons 77; and the Big Bang 8-9
pulsating red giant 34-6

quarks 77; and the Universe 8-9
quasars 13, 14-15, 21, 77

radio source 77; 3C 273 14
radio telescopes 8, 14-15
red dwarfs 32, 77
red giants 32, 34-6, 77
Ring Nebula 36
rings of planets 52-3
Ruskol, Evgenia 44

Safronov, Victor 44
Saturn 44, 49-53, 55; rings 52
Schmidt, Maarten 14
Sea of Fecundity 62
Solar System,
    comets and the birth of 46-7
    death of the Sun 68-9
    microcosm of Galaxy 42
    planets see planets
    rings 52-3
space missions 47, 58-9, 62
spiral galaxies 18-19, 24-5
stars,
    birth of 28-31; rebirth of 40-1
    converting hydrogen to helium 35
    dark 38-9
    dying 24-5; death 36-7
    main sequence 32, 76
    mass, size and temperature 32-5
    neutron 38-9
    number in, cannibals 22; galaxies 12, 18
    and proto-galaxies 12-13
    proto-stars 30-1
    in their prime 32-3; in middle age 34-5
Sun,
    birth of 42-5
    comets and the 46-7
    death of the 68-9
    mass, size and temperature 32-3
    and the Milky Way 12
    time for light from, to reach Earth 6
superclusters of galaxies 12-13
supergiant elliptical galaxies 22-3
supernova 41, 77; explosion 24, 36

Taurus, the Bull 36
telescopes, Hubble space 49; radio 8, 14-15; X-ray 41
temperature,
    Mars 58-9
    Pluto-Charon 49
    stars 32-5
    superhot gases 16
    Triton, coldest place in Solar System 55
Tharsis Ridge 58-9
Titan, Saturn's moon 55
Tombaugh, Clyde 48
Toomre, Alar and Juri 20
Triton, Neptune's moon 55

Uranus 48-51

Venus 56, 60-1
Viking (spacecraft) 58-9
Virgo 11

Wetherill, George 56, 62
Whipple, Fred 47
white dwarfs 32, 38-9, 40-1, 68, 77
Wolf, Max 16

X-rays 16, 40-1, 77

Zel'dovich, Yakov 13
Zwicky, Fritz 11, 38